A TRENCHERM
TO TH
EASTERN C
EDITED BY: JAME

GW00659692

CONTENTS

Published by
Bracken Publishing, Bracken House,
199a Holt Road, Cromer, Norfolk NR27 9JN

ISBN 1 871614 24 4

Printed by Broadgate Printers, Aylsham, Norfolk.
March 1996

FROM THE SAME PUBLISHER...

A5 size, 304 Pages of text

£11.95 from leading bookshops, or by mail order direct by mail order direct from publisher (see page one for address). Add £1.55 postage and packing (£13.50 including P&P)

IMPORTANT

Please note:-

1. Dishes listed are examples only. Menus change frequently, so they will not necessarily be available at all times.

2. Prices, where quoted, may change during the currency of this guide. Average a la carte prices are based on a three course meal without wine, unless otherwise stated.

3. Open hours refer to meals only, up until last orders are taken, unless otherwise stated.

4. Every effort is made to ensure accuracy, but inevitably circumstances alter and errors and omissions may occur. Therefore the publisher cannot accept liability for any consequences arising therefrom.

5. Your comments regarding establishments, whether featured or not, are especially welcome. All letters will be gratefully acknowledged, and correspondents who particularly impress will receive a free copy of the next edition.

6. This is a selection: it is not claimed that all the best establishments in the region are featured.

7. A note to proprietors: if your establishment is not featured, please do not be offended! The area covered is very large, and time limited. If you serve good food in pleasant surrounds, and would like to be considered for the next edition, please write and let us know.

INN RELIEF

Sue & Steve Dixon, MBII

Over 30 Years' experience in Licenced Catering Trade.

Recognised by

EGON RONAY, LES ROUTIERS & MOST LEADING PUB FOOD GUIDES

TEL 01440 62241 · MOBILE 0850 311218

WIN A LONG WEEKEND
FOR TWO IN ROME!

St Peter's, The Vatican

How to enter the Prize Draw

At the top of each page in the inns and pubs section you will see a 'trivia' question about the establishment featured on that page. Some of the clues are a little cryptic, some very straightforward; in most cases it may be fun to find out the answer for yourself, but in a few cases you will need to ask at the bar.

All you have to do is write the answer on the back of a receipt from that same inn or pub and send it to Bracken Publishing at the address shown on page one. You will also need to complete the entry form on page 7 and send that in with your first receipt. After that you may send in as many answers on receipts as you like (remembering to include your name and address each time), but only one per establishment. Each will count as an entry into the draw. The prize goes to the first name drawn.

▲▼▲

THE WEEKEND IN ROME INCLUDES:-
* Return flights from Stansted to Rome
* Transfer on arrival from airport to city centre
* Choice of three nights (one must be Saturday) bed and breakfast at 3-Star city-centre hotel, or 2 nights (incl. one Saturday) at a 4-Star hotel (no obligation to eat at the hotel)
* Information Guide to Rome
* Services of local agent
* Government Air Travel Duty.

THERE ARE NO 'TRIVIA' QUESTIONS IN THE HOTELS & RESTAU-RANTS SECTION, BUT THE READER WHO SUBMITS THE MOST RECEIPTS FROM THIS SECTION WILL WIN A MEAL FOR TWO AT ANY ESTABLISHMENT FEATURED IN THESE PAGES, INCLUDING DRINKS UP THE VALUE OF £20. IN THE EVENT OF A TIE THE ENTRY WITH THE GREATER TOTAL VALUE OF RECEIPTS WINS.

RULES

1. Only receipts from establishments featured in this edition will be accepted.

2. Only one receipt per establishment will qualify.

3. Only one entry form per person will be accepted.

4. Entrants must be aged 18 or over.

5. No photocopies of the entry form or receipts will be accepted (receipts are returnable on request).

6. The winner of the holiday is automatically disqualified from winning the meal for two.

7. Both prizes must be taken before December 31st, 1998, subject to availability.

8. Proprietors and staff of featured inns, pubs, hotels and restaurants may enter but should not submit receipts from their own establishments!

9. Closing date for entries is 31st Deecember, 1997. The draw will take place early in January 1998 and the winners notified as soon as possible. The names of the winners may be obtained by writing to the publisher.

▲▼▲

▲▼▲▼▲▼▲▼▲▼▲▼▲▼▲▼▲▼▲▼▲▼▲▼▲▼▲▼▲▼▲▼▲▼▲▼▲▼

ENTRY FORM FOR PRIZE DRAW-ROME

TITLE .... SURNAME ....

FORENAME ....

ADDRESS ....

....

.... POSTCODE ....

TELEPHONE NUMBER..
(WILL ONLY BE USED TO NOTIFY WINNERS)

I BOUGHT MY COPY OF TRENCHERMAN'S GUIDE AT: ....

....

I WOULD LIKE TO RECOMMEND THE FOLLOWING INNS/PUBS/HOTELS/
RESTAURANTS **(CONTINUE OVERLEAF IF NECESSARY)**:-

....

....

....

....

....

....

....

....

....

PLEASE ENTER ME FOR THE PRIZE DRAW AND/OR FREE MEAL
COMPETITION. I HAVE READ AND UNDERSTOOD THE RULES.
I AM OVER 18.

SIGNED...DATE ....

▲▼▲▼▲▼▲▼▲▼▲▼▲▼▲▼▲▼▲▼▲▼▲▼▲▼▲▼▲▼▲▼▲▼▲▼▲▼

I WOULD LIKE TO RECOMMEND THE FOLLOWING INNS/PUBS/HOTELS/ RESTAURANTS **(CONTINUED FROM PREVIOUS PAGE)**:-

RECIPES

HARICOT BEAN *&* TRUFFLE SOUP
(from The White Hart, Gt Yeldham, see page 206)

INGREDIENTS
500g haricot beans, soaked
overnight

4ozs butter for sweating

2 large onions, sliced

3 pints whipping cream

2tsp chopped truffles

salt & pepper

METHOD
Bring haricots to boil and strain
Bring to boil again in fresh salted water
Boil hard for 10 mins, then reduce heat
Simmer until tender (up to 1 hour)
Strain, but keep liquid
Sweat onions in butter until transparent
Add haricots and sweat for a few mins
Then add liquid and bring to boil
Add cream, boil and season
Purée and sieve (latter only if mix is very coarse)

CELERY, CIDER & STILTON CREAM

(from Richard Hughes of No. 24, Wymondham, see page 190)

INGREDIENTS - SERVES 4

50g butter
100g onion, finely sliced
1 head of celery, washed, peeled & chopped
50g flour
rosemary
thyme
250ml cider
250ml chicken/vegetable stock

METHOD

Simmer sliced onion gently in butter, without colour
Add chopped celery, simmer until soft
Add flour, cook out for further 5 mins, stirring thoroughly
Gradually add hot stock, then cider & herbs, simmer for 20 mins
Liquidise and pass through fine strainer

STILTON CREAM

50ml cream
50g grated stilton
50g parsley

Warm cream with grated stilton
Add parsley
Swirl generously and decoratively onto hot soup

LAMB STEAK WITH DILL & CUCUMBER SAUCE

(from Dutch Barn, Southwold, see page 198)

INGREDIENTS

2 x 6oz lamb steaks

½ pint double cream

pinch of garlic salt

1 tsp dill

3" slice of cucumber, cut into thin strips

METHOD

Sauté lamb steaks in oil until cooked - should be pink in centre
Remove steaks from pan, drain off fat from pan
Add to pan cream, salt, dill - simmer until cream thickens
Add cucumber
Return steaks to the sauce and simmer gently for 3 - 5 mins
Place steaks on plate and pour over sauce

Serve with new potatoes

MEDALLIONS OF SCOTTISH VENISON TOPPED WITH FLASH-FRIED PIGEON BREASTS & LAYERED WITH A CLASSICAL PEASE PUDDING

(from Swan Hotel, Southwold - see page 196)

INGREDIENTS - SERVES 4

8 small medallions of venison about ¼" thick

4 boneless pigeon breasts

olive oil and seasonings

PEASE PUDDING:

4ozs yellow split peas, soaked

½ pint chicken stock

1oz diced carrot

1oz chopped onion

1oz bacon trimmings

1oz butter

METHOD

PEASE PUDDING:
Place all ingredients (except butter) in a saucepan with tight-fitting lid
Bring to boil, then place in moderate oven (180°c - 200°c) for approx. 2 hours
Pass all ingredients through sieve or liquidise
Add butter, check consistency

TO FINISH:
Brush pigeon breasts with olive oil and season well
Lightly fry for 2 - 3 mins on each side
Put aside to keep warm
Do exactly the same with venison
Assemble pease pudding and venison alternately
Fan out pigeon breasts on top layer of pease pudding

Serve accompanied with roasted shallots, garlic cloves and a rich port wine sauce - enjoy!

DOUBLE-BAKED GOATS' CHEESE SOUFFLÉ WITH APPLE & WALNUT SALAD

(from Pheasant, Keyston, see page 169)

INGREDIENTS - SERVES 8

350ml milk	60g strong flour
40g butter	150g goats' cheese
½ tsp mustard	5 egg yolks
5 egg whites	salt & pepper
1 Granny Smith apple,	2 sticks celery
75g walnuts, chopped small	mixed salad
goats' cheese	200g breadcrumbs

METHOD

Make a roux with the butter and flour
Add milk slowly, stirring constantly
When you have added all the milk, add the cheese
Should have thick, paste-like consistency - leave to cool
Butter ramekins with softened butter, coat with breadcrumbs
Add egg yolks to cooled mixture and season with salt, pepper & mustard
Whip egg whites to a soft peak and very gently fold into the cheese mixture
Fill moulds to top (option to place small piece of cheese in middle of each soufflé)
Cook in bain marie in oven for about 20 mins at 160°c

Mix together apple, celery and walnuts, bind with mayonnaise
When soufflés are ready cool them and refrigerate (up to 24hrs)
To reheat, place on baking tray (out of the ramekin) until breadrumbs are lightly toasted and soufflé is doubled in size

TO SERVE:
Place quenelles of the celery, apple and walnuts around the plate, along with small pieces of cheese. Serve the soufflé on top of the mixed salad

RISOTTO FLORENTINE
from Old Bridge Hotel, Huntingdon, see page 173)

INGREDIENTS

2ozs finely chopped onion

4ozs shredded spinach

3ozs risotto rice (Vialone Nano if available)

1 glass white wine

vegetable stock

METHOD

Sweat off the onion in olive oil until translucent

Add spinach and stir for a few mins

Add in risotto rice and continue stirring until rice has taken up any excess liquid

Pour in white wine, stir until this is also absorbed

Continue to add in stock, little at a time, stirring to prevent rice sticking, for 15 - 20 mins; rice should be soft but not mushy

Correct seasoning and stir in a little whole butter

TO FINISH:

Put heaped serving spoonful of hot cooked rice in middle of a bowl

Poach one or two eggs in acidulated water for 2 -3 mins, keeping yolks soft

Put these on top of risotto

Quickly reduce some double cream in saucepan and pour this over rice and eggs

Garnish with some shaved parmesan cheese & freshly grated black pepper

CARROT ROULADE FILLED WITH STILTON & WALNUT SERVED WITH CUMBERLAND SAUCE

(from Farmhouse Feast, Roxwell, see page 215)

INGREDIENTS

1lb grated carrots	2 egg yolks
4 egg whites	¼ tsp ground coriander
1oz wholemeal breadcrumbs	salt & grnd black pepper

FILLING:

4ozs low fat cheese	4ozs vegetarian stilton
2 tbsp finely cut chives	2ozs chopped walnuts
ground black pepper	

SAUCE:

2 finely chopped shallots	2 tbsp redcurrant jelly
juice & finely sliced rind of 1 lemon & 1 orange	
¼ pint port	1 tbsp wine vinegar
pinch ground ginger	pinch cayenne pepper
pinch salt	

METHOD

Pre-heat oven to 200°c (400°f or mark 6)
Line bottom and sides of 12" x 8" (30 x 20cm) Swiss roll tin with non-stick parchment paper
Drain the carrot, then mix with egg yolks, coriander, breadrcumbs & seasoning
Whisk the egg whites until they are fairly stiff
Using a metal spoon gradually fold in one spoon of egg white into the carrot mixture, then add the remainder
Spread into tin; bake for 10-15 mins until firm to touch
Cover with teatowel and leave to cool
Blend all filling ingredients together
Turn roulade onto greaseproof paper and peel off lining paper
Spread filling over surface of roulade
Roll into Swiss roll shape, using greaseproof to keep roulade in shape
For the sauce, blanch the shallots in boiling water for two mins, drain
Blanch strips of lemon & orange for one minute, drain
Melt redcurrant jelly, add shallots, rind, port & vinegar - mix well
Add ginger, salt & pepper
Cook gently to reduce by one third

FRESH LOBSTER BISQUE WITH CAYENNE

(from The Punch Bowl, High Easter, see page 216)

INGREDIENTS

4 cooked lobsters

3lbs onions

3lbs carrots

6ozs flour

head of celery

3 tbspns Cognac

2ozs butter

3 bottles white wine (decent!)

3 bouquets garnis

8ozs tomato purée

1 tspn cayenne pepper

1 pint double cream

seasoning to taste

METHOD

Roughly chop vegetables and gently sauté with butter in large saucepan until onions are clear
Take off the heat and add flour, tomato purée & Cognac

Cut lobsters lengthways, crack claws and put into pot
Return saucepan to moderate heat, cooking out the flour and stirring continuously
Add white wine, refill the bottles with water and add this
Add bouquets garnis and season with WHITE ground pepper (black will mark the soup)
Gently bring to boil, let soup 'rest'
When cold, strain through fine sieve
Just before serving, add cream and serve hot

You will be amazed at the depth of flavour the lobsters provide, and although not one of the cheapest soups to make, probably one of the most delicious!

MUSSEL CRESS SOUP
(from Ray Morrison of The Old Hoops, Saffron Walden, see page 205)

INGREDIENTS

1 quart fresh mussels, cleaned and de-bearded

half-bottle dry white wine

6 shallots, finely chopped

2 sticks celery, finely chopped

whipping cream

1½ozs flour

1½ozs butter

1 large potato, diced small

handful of fresh watercress leaves, chopped

seasoning to taste

METHOD

Place mussels in large pan with wine, shallots & celery
Cook on high heat, stirring occasionally, until shells have opened - discard shells which do not open
Remove from heat, drain liquid and reserve
Remove mussels from shells - discard shells
Double the quantity of liquid with whipping cream
Bring to boil
Thicken with flour & butter worked together into smooth paste
When thickened to soup consistency, add potato
Then add mussels
Simmer for 2 -3 mins
Finish with watercress leaves and season to taste

VICHYSSOISE WITH SMOKED HADDOCK
(from Morston Hall, see page 183)

INGREDIENTS

6 leeks (white parts only)

1½ pints light chicken stock

2 medium potatoes, peeled and chopped

2 large fillets of undyed smoked haddock, skinned

1 pint milk

½ onion, chopped

1 bay leaf

seasoning

sprigs of thyme

METHOD

Simmer leeks in chicken stock, cover for 20 mins

Meanwhile, place haddock on roasting tray, cover with onion, milk, thyme & bay leaf

Poach in moderate oven (350f, 175c, gas mark 4) until fish flakes away (c. 20 mins)

Add potato, salt & pepper to leeks & stock and cook until potatoes are soft

Liquidise and put through sieve

Take haddock from oven and pour liquid from it into soup

Flake fish into chunky pieces then place in soup

WARM SMOKED HADDOCK MOUSSE WITH CRUNCHY VEGETABLES WITH ORANGE DRESSING

(from Scutchers Bistro, Long Melford, see page 204)

INGREDIENTS

10ozs undyed smoked haddock

3 eggs

7ozs creme fraiche

cayenne pepper

2 carrots

2 raw beetroots

2 courgettes

3 oranges

1 lemon

¼ pint extra virgin olive oil

METHOD

Skin the haddock and puree in a food processor

Add the eggs, season with cayenne

Add creme fraiche and mix for a few seconds only

Butter eight medium-size ramekins and fill with mixture

Cook in water bath for 40 mins at 170c

Meanwhile, peel carrots and beetroot

Cut all vegetables into matchstick-size pieces

Squeeze the oranges and lemon and mix with olive oil

To serve, scatter the vegetables on a warm plate, spoon on orange dressing

When mousses are cooked let cool for a few mins

Turn out, placing the mousse in the middle of the plate

Serve at once

BRANDADE OF SMOKED HADDOCK WITH A SALAD OF FINE HARICOTS VERTS & BLACK OLIVES

(from Sheen Mill Hotel, Melbourn, see page 175)

INGREDIENTS

2 medium-sized jacket potatoes

2 leaves of gelatine

2 fillets undyed smoked haddock, skinned & boned

10 fl ozs milk

2 whites of leek

3 cloves garlic

2 fl ozs double cream per person

salt & pepper

dash lemon juice & brandy

2ozs fine Kenya beans per person

hazelnut oil for dressing

½oz chopped black olives per person

dill & tomato to garnish

METHOD

Cook potatoes in oven until soft; skin and mash until smooth
Soak gelatine in water

Gently poach haddock in milk with leeks, garlic and salt & pepper to taste until cooked (5 - 8 mins)
Strain off fish & leek and blend in food processor; reserve poaching liquid
Squeeze any excess water from gelatine and dissolve it in hot poaching liquor
Mix in fish & leeks
Mix this together with mashed potao and allow to cool before putting in fridge to set
Allowing 2ozs base mix per person, gently fold in 2 fl ozs semi-whipped double cream
Add dash of lemon juice & brandy, adjust seasoning to taste
Gently whisk mixture until you see slight thickening
Refrigerate for one hour

For the salad, blanch fine beans, run under cold water for a few mins to refresh, drain
When dry, dress in hazelnut oil, salt & pepper, and add chopped black olives
Present quenelle of brandade on bed of green beans & olives
Garnish with sprig of dill & tomato concasse

TARAMASALATA
(from The Captain's Table, Woodbridge, see page 201)

INGREDIENTS

8ozs brown bread crumbs

8tbsp milk

1 clove garlic

1lb smoked cod roe, chopped

1 pint vegetable oil

juice of one lemon

8tbsp yoghurt (Greek sheep's is best)

METHOD

Blend together bread crumbs, milk and garlic in blender
Add cod roe
Blend thoroughly and slowly add vegetable oil
Add lemon juice
Add yoghurt
Blend again

Often served with hot pitta bread.

LOWESTOFT KIPPER & WHISKY PATÉ

(from Karen Aldridge, Chef de Partie, Swan Hotel, Southwold, sister hotel to The Cricketers, Reydon, see page 194)

INGREDIENTS (SERVES 8 - 10)

5 x kippers

4 x rashers of bacon, sliced into thin strips

52 x onions, sliced

¼ pint cream

½lb butter

lemon juice

seasoning

2 x large potatoes, peeled and diced small

2 x tots whisky

METHOD

Gently cook potatoes and onions in butter until soft
Oven-bake kippers; remove skin and bones by sieving
Blend kippers, potatoes and onions with cream until smooth
Gradually add melted butter
Fry bacon in a little oil
Fold in bacon, lemon juice, seasoning and whisky
Pour into cling film-lined terrine mould and refrigerate to set

Serve with hot granary toast and horseradish cream

WARM SMOKED SALMON & A TART OF QUAILS' EGGS WITH BEURRE BLANC
(from Adlard's of Norwich, see page 188)

INGREDIENTS (SERVES 4)

1lb fillet of smoked salmon (centre section)

6 quails eggs (2 for spares)

4 cooked tarts about 1½ - 2" across, of short crust pastry

SAUCE:

2 big shallots, finely diced

200ml dry white wine

50ml white wine vinegar

1 tbsp double cream

250gm unsalted butter

METHOD

SAUCE:
Reduce first three ingredients until dry (not burnt)
Add double cream, boil up and add hard butter in small amount, each time whisking it in, careful to keep temperature warm to hot - if sauce is too cold or hot it will split - consistency should be creamy
Season and keep warm

EGGS:
Cook in boiling water for 2mins 15 secs and refresh in cold water
Peel eggs - ideally leave in fridge overnight in water and peel next day
Should be soft-boiled
Cut salmon in ¼" thick pieces (2 per person)

TO FINISH:
Warm up eggs in near-boiling water for 30 secs
Drain and season
Warm tarts and fill with eggs
Cook salmon in steamer or char-grill plate so it is cooked on outside and warm, but uncooked in middle

Serve

POTATO PANCAKES WITH SEARED SALMON, SMOKED SALMON, CREME FRAICHE & CAVIAR

(from The Three Horseshoes, Madingley, see page 174)

INGREDIENTS - SERVES 4

1lb mashed potato

3tsp flour

3 eggs

4 egg whites, whipped

4ozs double cream

seasoning

4ozs salmon seared on grill

1oz smoked salmon

creme fraiche, caviar & dill to garnish

METHOD

Mix all ingredients together except egg whites - add them at the last!

WARM POTATO LATKES WITH SMOKED SALMON & CREAM

(from Old Bridge Hotel, Huntingdon, see page 173)

INGREDIENTS

4 medium-sized potatoes, peeled and grated

2 whole eggs

½ onion, chopped

½ bunch chives

4 - 6 ozs plain flour

2tsp baking powder

salt & pepper

lemon juice

cup of double cream

small quantity clarified butter

smoked salmon, sliced

sprig of dill

little ground paprika

METHOD

Wash and squeeze-dry potatoes to remove excess starch
Purée together in food processor the eggs, onion, chives & potato
Add flour, then baking powder, mix in
Adjust seasoning to taste
This is the batter, and should hold together like a drop-scone

Add lemon juice to cream to make soured cream
Stir until it thickens
Heat clarified butter in thick-bottomed pan until it is hot but not smoking
Put in a good tablespoon of batter, fry for two mins
Turn and cook until both sides are golden brown
Keep cooked latkes warm while cooking others

Arrange cooked latkes on a plate
Top with generous amount of sliced smoked salmon
Pipe or spoon some of the soured cream onto the plate
Garnish with dill
Dust plate with paprika

SAVOURY PANCAKES BEATRIX
(from The Pier, Harwich, see page 209)

INGREDIENTS (SERVES 4)

PANCAKES:

4ozs plain flour

1 egg (size 2)

8 fl ozs milk

1oz butter

chopped parsley, dill & chives

pinch salt & pepper

FILLING:

2 smoked trout

2ozs fish veloute

2 fl ozs double cream

grated fresh horseradish

salt & mill pepper

METHOD

PANCAKE BATTER (FOR 8 PANCAKES):
Place flour, seasoning & egg in bowl, add a little milk, blend to a smooth paste
Gradually beat in remaining milk
Melt butter to nut-brown colour and whisk in thoroughly
Add chopped herbs

FILLING:
Fillet smoked trout and reserve
In a bowl combine fish veloute with double cream, horseradish & seasoning
Add flaked smoked trout and fold together
Lay eight pancakes on work surface and divide filling between them
Fold carefully and place either in one large or four individual oven/tableware dishes
Bake in medium oven for 8-10 mins
Garnish with chopped mixed herbs and serve immediately

CRAB ANDRÉE
(from Little Hammonds, Ingatestone, see page 213)

INGREDIENTS (SERVES 6)

½lb saffron rice (rice cooked with saffron)

4ozs chopped cooked spinach

4ozs fresh picked crab

½ pint natural yoghurt

2 tbsp mayonnaise

1 tbsp turmeric

salt & pepper to taste

DRESSING:

¼ pint olive oil

½ oz saffron

tsp English mustard

1 clove chopped garlic

2ozs white wine vinegar

salt & pepper to season

METHOD

CRAB MIX:
Mix ingredients together and press firmly into four ramekin dishes
When packed firmly tip out onto serving plate

DRESSING:
In a bowl quickly whisk the vinegar mustard garlic and saffron, adding in slowly the oil and seasoning
To ensure the flavour, do not use for one hour to let the saffron infuse with the oil and vinegar
Dressing will keep in a bottle for up to two weeks

TIGER PRAWNS PAN-FRIED WITH TOMATO & BASIL PISTOU

(from Riverside Restaurant, Woodbridge, see page 200)

INGREDIENTS (SERVES 4)

20 tiger prawns, shelled and raw

5 large beef tomatoes

4 shallots, peeled and finely chopped

1 bunch fresh basil, shredded

3 tbsp olive oil

pinch ground coriander

METHOD

Blanch tomatoes in boiling water for 10 seconds
Refresh in iced water until completely cold
Drain and remove skins
Cut into quarters and de-seed
Bind together tomatoes, shallots and basil with three tbsp olive oil and pinch of coriander
Gently heat in frying pan 1 tbsp of olive oil and add tiger prawns
Fry for two mins on each side and gently add tomato mixture
Divide into four serving dishes with some freshly cooked egg pasta

SAUTE OF CHICKEN LIVERS IN MADEIRA & CREAM

(from William Bavin of Weavers, Diss, see page 191)

INGREDIENTS (PER PERSON)

3ozs chicken livers

1 tbsp medium Madeira

2 tbsp double cream

salt & pepper

5½oz butter

1 slice toasting bread

METHOD

Trim livers, removing any sinuous fat
Cut to equal squares
Melt butter in sauté pan
Seal livers and season
Add Madeira
Add double cream and reduce to a syrup
Serve immediately onto hot toast and garnish with small dressed salad.

NB: do not allow livers to overcook; they should be spongy and pink inside.

AUTUMN PIGEON
(from Sue Woods, chef properietor of the Old Counting House, Haughley - see page 203)

INGREDIENTS - SERVES 4

8 pigeon breasts

2 - 3 ozs butter

2 tblsp bramble jelly

2 tblsp apple jelly

4 tblsp red wine

METHOD

Pan-fry the pigeon breasts in the butter for 5 - 10 mins depending on size - should be pink in middle
Remove breasts from pan and keep warm
To the pan juices add wine and jellies
Boil rapidly to reduce by half
Pour over pigeon breasts to glaze
Garnish with blackberries and apple slices

PIGEON BREASTS IN A CREAM SAUCE WITH BACON & MUSHROOMS

(from Crown Hotel, Wells, see page 182)

INGREDIENTS (SERVES 4)

12 pigeon breasts

½ pint bechamel sauce

4 slices back bacon (smoked or
unsmoked), chopped

4ozs sliced button mushrooms

4fl ozs medium/dry white wine

2fl ozs double cream

½ medium onion, finely diced

½oz unsalted butter

seasoning to taste

METHOD

Seal pigeon breasts in butter and remove from pan
Sweat off bacon, mushrooms and onion and remove from pan
Add wine to pan, reduce by half
Add bechamel, replace pigeon and bacon mix
Just before serving finish with cream
Season to taste

RIVERSIDE SEAFOOD GUMBO

(from Riverside Restaurant, Woodbridge, see page 200)

INGREDIENTS (SERVES 6)

1lb cooked prawns
¼lb butter
1lb okra, sliced
2 onions, chopped
2 tbsp flour
1 cup tomatoes, sliced
1lb mixed fish (red snapper, mussels, scallops etc)
2 tsp salt
1 clove garlic, minced
½lb mixed peppers, chopped
1 tbsp Worcester sauce
1lb crab claws
6 drops tabasco sauce
4 cups cooked wild rice

METHOD

Sauté prawns in half the butter
Heat remaining butter in large pan
Add okra and cook, stirring until tender
Then add onions and cook for 6 mins
Add flour and stir until smooth
Add tomatoes, cook further 6 mins
Now combine fish juices with ¼ pint water, add to tomatoes and okra
Add salt, garlic and mixed peppers
Simmer for one hour
12 mins before end of cooking time add fish & prawns, cook over low heat
Add Worcester sauce, crab claws and tabasco
Turn heat to medium for just 2 mins
Serve on bed of hot cooked wild rice.

CALDEIRADA A FRAGATEIRO - FISH CASSEROLE, BARGEE STYLE

(from Alvaro's, Westcliffe, see page 210)

INGREDIENTS

1lb halibut (or any ombination of firm white fish), skinned, boned & cut into 1" cubes

8 scampi, shelled

8 scallops (and/or prepared squid), cut into squares

2 onions, chopped

3 - 4 large ripe tomatoes, peeled & roughly chopped

2 (minimum) large cloves of garlic, crushed

1lb potatoes, peeled & thinly sliced

2 tbsps parsley (incl. stalks), roughly chopped

1 fresh bayleaf (or 2 dried)

1 cup dry white wine

seasoning to taste

3 tbsp extra virgin olive oil (pref. Portuguese, but Greek will do)

1 small green pepper, de-seeded & thinly sliced (optional)

METHOD

In large pan saute the onion & bayleaf gently in olive oil until softened but not browned
Add garlic and stir
In layers over the onion first place the tomatoes (and optional green pepper), then potatoes, halibut, scampi & scallops (and/or squid)
Sprinkle with parsley & season well
Add wine
Bring to gentle simmer
Cover and simmer for 20 mins, or until potato & fish are just cooked

Serve with fresh crusty bread and side salad

GRILLED & MARINATED RED MULLET WITH PROVENCAL VEGETABLES, MINT & GARLIC OIL

(from No 24 Restaurant, Wymondham, see page 190)

INGREDIENTS

Red mullet fillets, scaled and boned, marinaded for 2 hours

MARINADE:

½ cup olive oil

¼ cup wine vinegar

½ cup white wine

lemon juice

½ tsp mint sauce

½ tsp garlic

salt & black pepper

chopped parsley

ROASTED VEGETABLES:

aubergine

courgettes

red, green & yellow peppers

plum tomatoes

Cut into 4cm dice, roast in a little of the marinade

To serve: simply place the vegetables on warm plate, top with red mullet and dressed seasonal leaf for a simple but stunning starter or light snack.

ROASTED FILLET OF SEA BASS
with Ricard & coriander-flavoured tomato salsa

(from Kirk Ellingham, chef de partie, Knife & Cleaver, Houghton Conquest - see page 167)

INGREDIENTS (SERVES 4)

4 medium sized sea bass fillets, trimmed & scaled

8 large coriander leaves

4 small bunches cornsalad or similar leaves

FOR THE SAUCE

20 firm tomatoes

bunch of coriander, chopped

200ml virgin olive oil

50ml Ricard

100ml lemon juice

100ml white wine

2 tbsp sugar

10 large shallots, finely diced

seasoning

METHOD

Score the skin of prepared bass fillets to stop them curling
Cut gently under skin and fill cuts with coriander leaves
Lightly brush with olive oil and season
Place in a clean hot pan and seal, skin down
Turn over, place pan in medium oven, roast until skin side is crisp and flesh tender

SALSA
Blanch tomatoes by scoring the top and coring, then immersing in boiling water for 10 secs, then refresh in ice
Skin, de-seed and chop into medium-sized dice
Chop the shallots and coriander
Sweat the shallots in the olive oil until translucent
Add tomatoes & coriander
Remove from heat, add wine, lemon juice & sugar
Adjust to taste, return to heat, add Ricard and cook for 3 mins
Remove from heat and keep warm
Tomatoes should be firm and salsa warm (not hot)

To serve: place salsa around the edge of the plates, put a small pile of leaves in the centre and arrange sea bass on top

SEA BASS IN FILO PASTRY WITH SORREL SAUCE

(from David White of The Duke of York, Billericay, see page 212)

INGREDIENTS

4 x 6ozs portions filleted bass (ensure there are no bones or skin)

1 large onion

2 glasses white wine

½ pint cream

2 sheets filo pastry

4 - 5ozs fresh sorrel

juice of ½ lemon

2ozs butter

METHOD

Preheat oven to 240c (475f) gas mark 8
Melt butter
Lay out filo pastry on board
Brush one sheet with butter, place second sheet over first
Place sea bass onto pastry
Put half the sorrel onto fish
Fold pastry over fish and wrap into parcel
Place onto greased baking tray, brush with remaining butter
Put in oven for 10 - 15 mins

SAUCE:

Reduce wine and cream in pan with diced onions & shredded sorrel
Add lemon juice, salt & pepper to taste

Pour sauce onto plate and place parcel on top. Garnish with lemon wedges.

MEDALLIONS OF MONKFISH WITH CUCUMBER IN A CREAMY SHERRY SAUCE

(from Quiggins, Wrentham, see page 193)

INGREDIENTS (SERVES 4)

24ozs monkfish, cut into medallions

½ cucumber, peeled, de-seeded and diced

2 medium onions, finely chopped

200ml amontillado sherry

100ml double cream

cayenne pepper or chilli sauce to taste

basil to taste

salt & pepper

virgin olive oil

METHOD

Add 2 tablespoons oil to a hot wok and soften onions until starting to colour

De-glaze with sherry and reduce to approx. half the volume

Add cream, cayenne, basil and seasoning to taste

Simmer until sauce is smooth - if necessary, thicken with roux blond

Heat another 2 tablespoons of oil in second wok until just smoking

Quickly seal medallions of monkfish

When they start to curl remove from wok and add to sauce

Toss diced cucumber in second wok for 45-60 seconds, then add to sauce

Simmer for 5-6 mins, adjusting seasoning if necessary

Serve immediately

MONKFISH ROASTED IN SAFFRON BUTTER WITH FLAGEOLETS & BACON

from Fen House, Littleport, see page 178)

INGREDIENTS (SERVES 4)

1½lbs monkfish

3ozs butter

generous pinch saffron

15ozs tin green flageolets

6ozs gammon steak

small glass dry white wine

2ozs butter

chopped parsley

2 chopped shallots

5 fl ozs double cream

METHOD

Melt the first 3ozs butter to liquid and add saffron (oil will extract the colour from the saffron)
Leave to stand until set
Lay the monkfish fillets on a buttered oven-proof dish and coat with half of the saffron butter
Roast in an oven for about 10 mins, depending on size
Cut the gammon into small batons and saute lightly in butter; reserve
Remove monkfish and keep warm
Pour juices into shallow sauce pan and add the chopped shallots.
Cook for 2 mins and add white wine
Reduce the liquid until almost dry
Add the cream and continue to reduce
When the sauce is about the thickness of single cream, remove from the heat and allow to cool slightly.
Mix in the remaining saffron butter
Heat the flageolets in butter
Mix in the gammon

TO SERVE:
A small heap of flegeolets in centre of plate. With a sharp knife slice the monkfish at a shallow angle. Pour the sauce around the flageolets and arrange monkfish on top. Decorate with chopped parsley.

SEA BREAM BAKED "EN PAPILLOTE"
(from Lloyd's Restaurant, Norwich, see page 187)

INGREDIENTS

4 fillets sea bream

4 spring onions, finely chopped

small knob of fresh root ginger, peeled
and cut into julienne strips

soy sauce

salt & black pepper to season

little melted butter

4 sheets greaseproof paper cut into butterfly or heart shape - large enough to enclose the
fish with space spare around the edges

METHOD

Lightly butter right hand side of greaseproof shapes
Place bream fillets on this half
Sprinkle with root ginger, spring onions & approx. ½ tsp soy sauce
Season lightly
Fold over remaining half of paper to enclose, and pleat edge to seal securely
Place on a baking sheet in pre-heated oven 150c (gas mark 4) for 15 - 20 mins, or until
packets are well puffed-up
Serve immediately

ROGNONS AU COGNAC
(from The Old Counting House, Haughley, see page 203)

INGREDIENTS (SERVES 2)

8 lambs' kidneys, sliced

½ medium onion, finely chopped

4 large mushrooms, sliced

2 tbsp brandy

¼ pint cream

6 crushed juniper berries

1oz butter

seasoning

METHOD

Gently sauté onion in butter until soft but not brown

Increase heat, add kidneys and mushrooms, brown them

Add brandy and juniper berries, cook for one minute

Add cream

Boil rapidly until sauce has thickened, being careful not to overcook kidneys (should be pink in middle)

Serve with selection of fresh seasonal vegetables

MEDALLIONS OF SCOTTISH VENISON TOPPED WITH FLASH-FRIED PIGEON BREASTS & LAYERED WITH A CLASSICAL PEASE PUDDING

(from Swan Hotel, Southwold - see page 196)

INGREDIENTS - SERVES 4

8 small medallions of venison about ¼"
thick

4 boneless pigeon breasts

olive oil and seasonings

PEASE PUDDING:

4ozs yellow split peas, soaked

½ pint chicken stock

1oz diced carrot

1oz chopped onion

1oz bacon trimmings

1oz butter

METHOD

PEASE PUDDING:
Place all ingredients (except butter) in a saucepan with tight-fitting lid
Bring to boil, then place in moderate oven (180°c - 200°c) for approx. 2 hours
Pass all ingredients through sieve or liquidise
Add butter, check consistency

TO FINISH:
Brush pigeon breasts with olive oil and season well
Lightly fry for 2 - 3 mins on each side
Put aside to keep warm
Do exactly the same with venison
Assemble pease pudding and venison alternately
Fan out pigeon breasts on top layer of pease pudding

Serve accompanied with roasted shallots, garlic cloves and a rich port wine sauce - enjoy!

MEDALLIONS OF VENISON TOPPED WITH GOAT'S CHEESE & WALNUT MOUSSE, WALNUT VINEGAR

(from Le Talbooth, Dedham, see page 208)

INGREDIENTS (SERVES 4)

8 x 4oz loin venison medallions	6ozs soft milk goat's cheese
2oz chopped peeled walnuts	2lbs fresh leaf spinach
⅛ pint walnut vinegar	1 pint venison stock
3ozs butter	2 large carrots
4 shallots	2 egg yolks
nutmeg	1 tbsp chopped coriander leaf
salt & pepper, sugar	(keep stalks)

METHOD - MOUSSE:

Allow cheese to warm to room temp. Add walnuts and egg yolks, mix in well. Mould into 8 equal-sized patties, a little smaller than medallions. Place in fridge for 1½ to 2 hours.

VEGETABLE GARNISHES:

Pick and thoroughly wash spinach, dry well. In saucepan melt 1½ozs butter, put in spinach, grate nutmeg onto it, season. Stir in until all spinach has gone soft, then drain & cool in sieve, squeeze out excess liquid. Line 4 medium ramekins with butter, then the bigger leaves of spinach. Equally divide the spinach among the ramekins and press down well. Cover with clingfilm and set aside. Cut carrots into fine, neat, even strips, keep trimmings. In saucepan, melt 1oz butter, add pinch sugar & 2 tbsp water, season, bring to boil. Put in carrot strips and cook until soft enough to twist around finger without snapping. Drain into colander and set aside.

SAUCE:

Heat saucepan until moderately hot. Slice shallot and any carrot trimmings, add to hot pan together with coriander stalks and drop or two of oils. Allow to colour a little, then add vinegar and allow to reduce almost completely. Now add stock, bring to boil, skim off scum, reduce (or if very strong thicken with arrowroot). Correct seasoning and keep hot.

ASSEMBLY:

Heat a good frying pan until very hot, add a little veg. oil and ½oz butter. Season venison with salt & pepper and fry for 3-4 mins each side, longer if preferred. Re-heat spinach ramekins in steamer for 6-7mins or in microwave. In small saucepan melt remaining butter and put in carrot strips & chopped coriander. Strain sauce and reboil. Once cooked, place venison on baking sheet and put goats' cheese pattie on each one and glaze under very hot grill. Turn out the spinach and place 1½" to left of centre on each of 4 hot plates. Neatly arrange the carrot strips 1" down from centre of plate. Place 1 medallion on spinach and 1 next to it on right.

Pour the sauce round and serve immediately.

WILD RABBIT WITH PRUNES, CIDER & MUSTARD

(from The Anchor Inn, Sutton Gault, see page 177)

INGREDIENTS - SERVES 4

1 large or 2 small wild (not farmed - important) rabbits, jointed into about 8 pieces

4ozs smoked streaky bacon, cut into 1" pieces

½ pint strong dry Suffolk cider

1 onion, coarsely chopped

groundnut oil for frying

4ozs whole prunes

1 good dessertspoon quality coarse-grain mustard

seasoned flour

small bunch fresh thyme

small sprig rosemary

2 bay leaves

METHOD

Sweat onion in a little oil until transparent
Add bacon, turn up heat and brown
Remove from frying pan, then add little more oil
Season rabbit pieces
Add rabbit to pan, brown lightly on moderate heat until sealed
Turn up heat, replace bacon and onion
Add cider, prunes, mustard & herbs, and enough water to just cover meat
Bring to boil, stirring bottom of pan to scrape crusty bits
Add a little salt and ground pepper
Put in covered casserole dish and bake in medium to slow oven for about 1½ hrs or until tender
Adjust seasoning to taste if necessary

Serve with simple baked potato or crusty bread, and a green vegetable or salad

ROAST BREAST OF CHICKEN WITH RABBIT WRAPPED IN SPINACH IN A MADEIRA & BLACKBERRY SAUCE

(from Anchor Hotel, Walberswick - see page 199)

INGREDIENTS - SERVES 4

4 breasts of chicken (boned)

1 rabbit

½lb fresh leaf spinach

seasoning

¼lb blackberries

¼ cup Madeira

½ pint chicken stock

flat leaf parsley (to garnish)

2 tblsp vegetable oil

METHOD

Slice open chicken lengthways (don't cut right through), fold open
Sprinkle on a little seasoning
Remove spinach leaves from stalks and wash in salt water
Thinly slice rabbit meat and season
Spread spinach leaves out over chicken breast (on upturned face only)
Lay rabbit on top of spinach and season
Roll chicken, spinach and rabbit into log shape
Heat frying pan and add a little oil
Seal both sides of the chicken in pan for about 30 secs each side
Place in medium hot oven for 10 mins
Using same frying pan, reduce chicken stock by half
Add Madeira and simmer for 2 mins
Add blackberries and simmer until chicken is ready

To serve: coat bottom of a plate with the sauce; slice chicken into three and arrange on top of the sauce; decorate with sprigs of parsley

TENDER CHICKEN BREAST IN A CREAM, CHEESE & BACON SAUCE
(from Wensum Lodge Hotel, Fakenham, see page 184)

INGREDIENTS

One boneless chicken breast

2 rashers smoked back bacon, cut into thin strips

15 fl ozs whipping cream

10 fl ozs dry white wine

2ozs grated mild cheddar cheese

4 tbsp vegetable oil

METHOD

Heat oil in saucepan and seal chicken without colouring

Place chicken on baking tray along with half the amount of wine

Cover with foil and cook in oven (gas mark 7) for 15-20 mins, turning once

Re-heat oil, sauté bacon

Add rest of wine and bring to boil

Then add cream and reduce by half

When chicken is cooked add to the pan and simmer for two mins

Add cheese, allow to melt, then serve

CHICKEN WITH BASIL
(from Brasteds, Norwich, see page 189)

INGREDIENTS
4 chicken breasts

2ozs butter

1 clove garlic, finely chopped

1 tbsp pesto sauce (which contains basil
and is available from any good deli)

5 fl ozs dry white wine

1 tbsp lemon juice

2 tbsp finely chopped parsley

salt & pepper

METHOD:

Thinly slice chicken breasts lengthways so that you have thin strips of meat

Fry the chicken in 1oz of butter until they turn white

Remove from pan and set on one side

In a medium saucepan melt the remaining butter and add garlic, pesto sauce, white wine &
lemon juice

Simmer for 4 mins

Add chicken and cook for further 5 mins

Sprinkle with chopped parsley and serve immediately

Suggest serve with deep-fried courgettes and tossed salad.

SZECHUAN DOUBLE-COOKED PORK

(from Kwok's Rendezvous, Ipswich, see page 202)

INGREDIENTS

12ozs boneless lean pork (can use beef or lamb), maybe left over from roast

1 large or 2 small stalks of spring onion, chopped

3 tbsp vegetable oil

3 cloves garlic, sliced and soaked in cold water for 30 mins, then drained

1 small tin sliced bamboo shoots

1 green pepper, cut into ¼" squares

1 red pepper, cut into ¼" squares

1 tbsp yellow bean sauce

1 small pinch ground red chilli (to taste)

2 tbsp dark soy sauce

2 tbsp cane sugar

METHOD

Steam or boil pork in stock, drain and cool
Cut into ⅛" thick slices (or use left over pieces from roast)
Heat oil in pan or wok
Put in garlic slices, spring onion, yellow bean sauce, ground chilli
Stir it all up
Add pork, bamboo shoots
Turn up heat, stir for 2 mins
Add sugar and soy sauce, continue stirring for 2 - 3 mins
If sauce starts to dry up add one or two tablespoons of chicken stock

Serve with rice.

BEEF PAUPIETTES
(from Edelweiss, Leigh-on-Sea, see page 211)

INGREDIENTS (SERVES 6)

3lbs top rump beef cut into 6 thin slices
6ozs minced beef

6 slices smoked streaky bacon
6 dill gherkins

2 onions

6 tsp sweet mustard
2tbsp olive oil

a carrot, small leek & parsnip
½ pint beef stock

3 bay leaves & pinch thyme
3 glasses red wine

2 tbsp flour
1 tbsp tomato paste

sprig of parsley
salt & pepper

METHOD

Lay out beef slices and spread on each first mustard, then minced beef, then layer of bacon, then onions
Add to each half a dill gherkin
Roll up meat like Swiss roll and secure at either end with cocktail sticks
Pour olive oil into casserole dish
Place in it the rolled-up meat (paupiettes) and heat over hot flame until browned
Remove from heat, add chopped carrot, leek & parsnip, plus thyme & bay leaves
Sprinkle flour over it, mix in tomato paste
Pour in red wine, top up with stock until covered
Place dish back on heat and bring to boil
Place dish in oven and cook for one hour at 200c or gas mark 6
Remove and strain sauce into pot, season, serve separately
Decorate paupiettes with half gherkins and parsley

Suggest serve with Swiss rosti potato

LAMB STEAK WITH DILL &
CUCUMBER SAUCE
(from Dutch Barn, Southwold, see page 198)

INGREDIENTS

2 x 6oz lamb steaks

½ pint double cream

pinch of garlic salt

1 tsp dill

3" slice of cucumber, cut into thin strips

METHOD

Sauté lamb steaks in oil until cooked - should be pink in centre
Remove steaks from pan, drain off fat from pan
Add to pan cream, salt, dill - simmer until cream thickens
Add cucumber
Return steaks to the sauce and simmer gently for 3 - 5 mins
Place steaks on plate and pour over sauce

Serve with new potatoes

CASSEROLED BRITISH LAMB WITH STILTON DUMPLINGS

(from The Bell Inn, Stilton, see page 171)

INGREDIENTS:	FOR THE DUMPLINGS
3lbs British lamb, diced	½ loaf white bread, diced
tbsp suntlower oil	5ozs self raising flour
1lb onions, diced	1 packet chives, chopped
1lb shallots, peeled	4ozs suet
1 tbsp English mustard	8ozs grated Stilton cheese
2ozs plain flour	½ pint milk
2 pints lamb stock	2 x size 3 eggs
1 pint medium sweet cider	
1 bouqet garni	
salt & black pepper	
5 large carrots, sliced	
2 old potatoes, diced	
10 baby sweetcorn, halved (optional)	
5 courgettes, sliced (optional)	

METHOD

Heat oil in large ovenproof casserole
Add diced onions & whole shallots, sweat without colour
Add diced lamb, cook until browned, then add mustard
Stir in flour to make a roux
Cook out for 2 - 3 mins
Gradually stir in stock & cider
Season well an add bouquet garni
Cover and cook in preheated oven for one hour
Add carrots & potatoes to casserole and cook further 15 mins

Meanwhile, prepare dumplings:
Mix together diced bread, flour, chives, suet & Stilton in bowl
Add milk & eggs
Divide mixture into approx. 18 portions
Remove casserole from oven
Stir in sweetcorn and courgettes
Drop dumplings into the liquid, cover casserole & cook for further 20 mins
Cook until dumplings are firm but light, ensuring vegetables are cooked and meat is tender

PAN-FRIED LAMB CUTLETS WITH MINT BUTTER SAUCE

(from Jonathan Nicholson, Head Chef at Congham Hall, see page 179)

INGREDIENTS FOR SAUCE

2 fl ozs white wine vinegar

4 sprigs mint (approx. 32 leaves in total)

12 black peppercorns, crushed

1 shallot

2 egg yolks

6 ozs clarified butter

pinch of salt

pinch cayenne pepper

¼ lemon

12 lamb cutlets

seasoning

1 fl oz olive oil

METHOD

Place white wine vinegar into pan
Pick tops off mint and reserve for garnish
Pick and chop 15 more leaves and reserve for finishing the sauce
Add remaining mint to vinegar along with crushed black peppercorns & shallot
Reduce until vinegar has almost evaporated, add 2 tbsp water
Allow to cool a few mins, then whisk in egg yolks
Place back on heat and continue whisking vigorously until ribbon stage is formed (do not scramble egs)
Remove from heat and add warm clarified butter

Season with salt and cayenne, add lemon juice
Pass through fine strainer, then add chopped mint
Keep in warm place up to 2 hrs - whisk before serving

Season lamb cutlets
Heat oil in pan, add cutlets, cook for 3 - 4 mins both sides
Allow to rest a few mins before serving - preferably pink

FLORENTINE SABLEE

(from Little Hammonds Restaurant, Ingatestone, see page 213)

INGREDIENTS - SERVES 6

6ozs butter

6½ ozs caster sugar

2ozs chopped cherries

2ozs chopped peel

4ozs sultanas

9ozs flaked almonds

2 fl ozs fresh cream

METHOD

Melt butter in saucepan, add sugar and bring to boil
Remove from heat and add fruit, then almonds
Stir well; when mixed, add cream
Spread on a silicon paper-lined baking tray
Bake at 180°c until golden - leave to set
Cut out discs of 7½ cms

SHORTBREAD BASE

INGREDIENTS

1lb plain flour

12ozs melted butter

4ozs caster sugar

METHOD

Mix all ingredients together into clear smooth paste and leave to rest briefly
Roll out and cut into 7½cm discs
Bake at 200°c for approx. 10 - 15 mins

Whip 1 pint of whipping cream and pipe onto shortbread bases
Lay slices of banana on top of cream
Place florentine on banana
Dust with icing sugar, garnish with sprig of fresh mint

STRAWBERRY & KIWI FRUIT SOFT MERINGUE PAVLOVA ROULADE

(from Les Snow, Head Chef at the Old Moot House, Castle Hedingham, see page 207)

INGREDIENTS - SERVES 10

6 egg whites (size 3)   12ozs caster sugar

2 tsp white wine vinegar
vanilla essence to taste

2 tbsp boiling water   pinch salt

2ozs caster sugar} for dusting
1 tsp cinnamon   }

FOR FILLING & DECORATION

1 pint double cream   12ozs strawberries
3 kiwi fruits

FOR BAKING

12" x 14" x 1" baking tray
silicone paper for lining

METHOD

Whisk egg whites and salt until stiff
Gradually add caster sugar, whisking all the time, until full peak
Continue whisking, add vinegar, vanilla and lastly boiling water
Whisk until smooth and silky

Line baking tray and spread meringue mix evenly
Dust with cinnamon/caster sugar mix
Bake for 20 mins on Gas 4, 180°c (350°f)
When baked, allow to cool thoroughly

Whip cream (may be flavoured with spirit or sweetened)
Turn out meringue carefully onto greaseproof paper
Spread cream evenly over meringue

Slice strawberries and kiwi fruits and lay onto cream evenly (reserve some fruit for decoration)
Carefully roll up meringue like a Swiss roll
Turn onto silver flat or serving dish
Decorate with reserved fruit and cream
Spin a little melted chocolate over the top .... Enjoy!

COLD LEMON SOUFFLÉ
(from Pepperpot Restaurant , West Runton, see page 186)

INGREDIENTS

2 lemons

3 eggs

1 pint double cream

½oz gelatine

½lb sugar

pistachio

toasted almond nibs

METHOD

Surround soufflé dish with greaseproof paper collar

Dissolve gelatine in juice of one lemon

Whisk the three egg yolks, sugar & juice from one lemon over a warm container (bain marie) until mixture thickens slightly (ribbon stage)

Add dissolved gelatine and allow to cool

When cold, fold in ¾ pint whipped cream, followed by beaten egg whites

Pour mixture into soufflé dish to the top of greaseproof collar and allow to set

Remove from refrigerator ½ hour before serving

ICED LEMON PARFAIT
(from Swan Hotel, Southwold, see page 196)

INGREDIENTS

3 egg yolks

3 egg whites

4ozs caster sugar

½ pint double or whipping cream

4 lemons, zested and squeezed for juice

METHOD

Line terrine mould with clingfilm

Place egg yolks and 2ozs of the sugar into a bowl and whisk until light in colour and thick

Loosely whip the cream and place in fridge

Pour lemon zest and juice into egg yolk mix and stir

Whip the whites and slowly add the other 2ozs of sugar until whites are stiff and peaky

Fold the cream into the egg yolk mix until clear

Then fold egg whites into the mixture carefully so as not to knock too much air out

When mixed, pour into terrine and cover with clingfilm

Freeze for 2 - 3 hours, serve with fruit sauce, fresh berries to decorate

BROWN BREAD ICE CREAM

(from Redcoats Farmhouse Hotel, Redcoats Green, see page 165)

INGREDIENTS

1 pint double cream

6ozs caster sugar

3 egg yolks

1 dessertspoon liquid glucose (optional but prevents ice cream from being hard)

4ozs brown breadcrumbs

2ozs brown sugar

METHOD

Caramelise the breadcrumbs and sugar by putting them in a moderate oven until browned - leave to cool

Place in liquidiser or food processor and reduce to fine crumb texture

Cream together the eggs and caster sugar until pale creamy colour

Then add glucose (warmed to make it runny)

Add cream and whip up to thick consistency

Fold in breadrumbs and freeze

MRS WRIGHT'S BUTTERSCOTCH TART

(from Punch Bowl Restaurant, High Easter, see page 216)

INGREDIENTS

6ozs dark brown sugar

6ozs salted butter

½ pint condensed milk

14ozs digestive biscuits & 4ozs salted butter

METHOD

Line base of 7" flan case with crushed biscuits by melting the butter, adding the biscuits and pressing firmly into the flan case

To make the tart, melt the remaining 6ozs butter and sugar VERY SLOWLY in a heavy-based copper saucepan
When mixed together, add milk and stir until all is combined
Slowly bring the mixture to the boil whilst being stirred
When thickened, pour onto flan case

BREAD & BUTTER PUDDING SUPREME

(from Quiggins Restaurant, Wrentham, see page 193)

INGREDIENTS

½ sliced white loaf with crusts removed

butter

apricot jam

Malmsey Madeira wine

4ozs raisins

½ pint milk

½ pint single cream

2 eggs

grated nutmeg

METHOD

Butter the bread and spread each slice with apricot jam

Cut slices into squares and arrange one layer in the bottom of a two-pint pie dish

Drizzle over Malmsey wine and scatter raisins on top

Continue in layers in this way until all the bread and raisins are used up

In a large bowl whisk together the eggs, milk and cream

Pour this mixture over the bread layers

Sprinkle with ground nutmeg

Leave to stand for 30 mins

When the bread is well soaked, place dish in centre of oven (150°c, gas mark 2) and bake for approx. two hours, or until pudding has risen and is golden brown

HOT SQUIDGY COFFEE &
WALNUT SPONGE

(from Weavers, Diss, see page 191)

INGREDIENTS

12ozs soft brown sugar

8ozs butter

6 tbsp coffee essence

2 eggs

8ozs self-raising flour

1 pint milk

4ozs walnut pieces

METHOD

Cream together 8ozs of soft brown sugar with the butter until light and creamy
Beat together eggs & coffee essence, add gradually to the creamed mixture
Add sieved flour and walnut pieces
Place in a deep buttered casserole dish
Mix remaining sugar with milk and pour on top of sponge
Bake at 320°f for 90 mins

MOHR IN HEMD WITH HOT CHOCOLATE SAUCE

(from Mirabelle Restaurant, West Runton, see page 185)

INGREDIENTS

100g plain chocolate

50g breadcrumbs

6 egg yoks

6 egg whites

vanilla essence

little butter

100g caster sugar

icing sugar

100g ground hazelnuts

SAUCE:

4 fl ozs double cream

1 dessertspoon honey

vanilla essence

3 - 4 ozs plain chocolate

METHOD

Whip egg yolks with half the caster sugar until frothy

Melt chocolate in saucepan or microwave, add to add mix

Mix hazelnuts & breadrumbs together, set aside

Whip egg white with rest of caster sugar to stiff 'snow'

Fold all together into egg yolk mix

Grease pudding bowl and dust in icing sugar, fill to approx. ¼ of mould

Put into bain-marie and bake at 180°c for 25 - 30 mins

Sauce:

Bring double cream, vanilla essence and honey to boil

Add chocolate (either in small pieces or pre-melted) with cream

Stir well, serve

Dip chocolate pudding onto warm plate

Pour chocolate sauce over

Finish with dollop of whipped cream

MILK CHOCOLATE & HAZELNUT TART
(from Congham Hall, Grimston, see page 179)

SERVES 8

STAGE ONE:

100g plain flour

50g butter

35g icing sugar

1 egg

salt

METHOD:

Cream butter and sugar, add egg, beat and fold in flour
Line a 12" - 15" diameter mould and cook blind

STAGE TWO:

150g milk chocolate, roughly chopped

100g hazelnuts

50g caster sugar

50g single cream

METHOD:

Roast hazelnuts and then blend while hot with sugar, then chocolate, then cream

STAGE THREE:

60g milk

2 eggs

250g double cream, softly whisked

METHOD:

Mix milk & eggs together and then add prepared purée from Stage Two
Whip double cream and fold into mixture
Pour into pre-cooked tart mould
Cook for 30-40 mins in pre-heated oven at 150°c

▲▼▲▼▲▼▲▼▲▼▲▼▲▼▲▼▲▼▲▼▲▼▲▼▲▼▲▼▲▼▲▼▲▼▲

INN & PUBS

▲▼▲▼▲▼▲▼▲▼▲▼▲▼▲▼▲▼▲▼▲▼▲▼▲▼▲▼▲▼▲▼▲▼▲▼▲

THE WHITE HART FREEHOUSE

1 Ongar Road, Abridge. Tel: (01992) 813104

Location : village centre, by River Roding. NB: no exit at jncn 5 on M11 for
southbound traffic (although it is planned).
Credit cards : not accepted.
Bitters : Marston's Pedigree, John Smiths, Courage Directors, Webster's
Yorkshire, occasional guest.
Lagers : Holsten Export, Fosters, Kronenbourg, Miller Lite.

Examples of bar meals (lunch & evening, except Mon evening): *steak & kidney pie; toad-in-the-hole; steaks; cod; scampi; cold platters; omelettes; jacket potatoes; sandwiches; many daily specials eg chicken & mushroom pie, seafood salad. Treacle pud; spotted dick; fruit pies; chocolate gateau.*

Examples of restaurant meals (as above): *camembert al chante; veal escalope with Madeira sauce; "White Hart" (fillet steak, marinated in red wine, charcoal grilled, filled with garlic cheese & pate, flamed in brandy - speciality); trout Aladdin (stuffed with seafood, cheese sauce, coated with almonds); Mexican bake (veg.). Trad. Sun. roasts (booking advised).*

If you think that inside the M25 is one huge concrete sprawl then you will surprised to discover this pleasant (if quite busy) village. Right by the river stands this fine example of the best kind of London pub, early Victorian, with high ceiling and windows, brass railings, immaculate furnishings and washrooms - the result of recent refurbishment. Outside, the hanging baskets are a picture in season, and the riverside patio and beer garden are very pleasant. Live entertainment is scheduled every Friday evening, but Elvis fans should keep Bank Holiday Mondays free, for that is when impersonator Bobby Day packs 'em in here. Terry and Karen Scales, owners since Jan. '94, are assisted by Ian as manager and chef. Pool and darts upstairs.

THE ALMA ARMS
Horseman Side, Navestock Side, Brentwood. Tel. (01277) 372629

Location: take Coxtie Green Road off A128 for 2 miles, right at
T-junction, then right into Dytchleys Lane, left at end
of lane - pub is 250 yds on right.
Credit cards: not accepted.
Bitters: Greene King Abbot, Rayments, Ridleys ESX.
Lagers: Kronenbourg, Fosters, Carlsberg.

Examples of bar meals (12 - 2:30pm, 7.00 - 9:30pm): *speciality homemade pies (eg steak, salmon & broccoli, chicken & mushroom, steak & stilton, Suffolk pie, steak & ale pie); home-made pasta & vegetarian dishes; mixed grill; fresh daily fish (eg salmon, trout); grills & steaks (incl. rump & T-bone); minted lamb; turkey steaks. Homemade desserts (eg cheesecake, sherry trifle, fruit crumbles, bread & butter pudding). Daily 3 course meal £6.45 (Sat. evening menu £8.95) Trad. Sun. roasts (incl. dessert) £6.75.*

NB: OPEN for home-cooked meals ALL DAY until 9:30pm daily inc. Sundays.

The Alma Arms is close to Brentwood and Harold Hill, and once off the main road the drive through the wooded and rolling Essex countryside is very pleasant, though not straightforward. Alan and Jane have run this busy rural inn for over 25 years, providing a varied homemade menu with the accent on value and freshness, complemented by a good range of ales and vast selection of wines. The inn was built in 1731 but only bore the 'Alma' title since the Crimean War battle of that name. The attractive bars are oak-beamed - the bar itself being brick with timber reliefs, the theme being continued to the fireplaces. A new addition is the very pleasant 40-seater Victorian conservatory where persons over 14 years old may dine, but for really warm days there is a patio to the front. Mentioned in several national guides. Large car park.

THE CROWN

Elsenham, nr Bishop's Stortford. Tel: (01279) 812827

Location : village centre.
Credit cards : Access, Visa, Diners, Amex, JCB.
Bitters : Crouch Vale Millennium Gold, Tetleys, guest.
Lagers : Carlsberg Export, Castlemaine, Carlsberg.

Examples of bar meals (lunch & evening daily except Sundays): *deep-fried bread baskets with various fillings; savoury stuffed pancakes; seafood mixed grill; sautéd chicken livers in crepe basket; steak & kidney pie; lamb turino; duck Marco Polo; fisherman's pie; vegetable lasagne; pork T-bone in Calvados; local fresh trout in shellfish sauce; steaks; daily specials eg barbecue ribs, fresh plaice filled with crab & prawns, casseroles. Lunch only: homemade Crown burgers; Braughing sausages (noted); chicken tikka; hot rib of beef. 15 home-made ice creams.*

The sheer extent and originality of the menu makes it all the more amazing that everything, even the ice cream, is home-made and fresh. This has not escaped the notice of most of the main national guides and especially that of local people, so booking is advised at peak times. All is of course cooked to order, but there are a number of quick items listed for those in a hurry at lunchtime. Around 350 years old, formerly three cottages and then a coaching inn (royalty is said to have stayed here), its antiquity can be seen in the split-level bar, with its old timbers and open fire, next to which is the intriguing 'Dingly Dell', a floral fantasy. Activity comes in the form of monthly quiz nights, darts and dominoes. Well behaved children welcome - swings in garden. Dining room available for wedding receptions (and funerals!). The patience and good humour of licensees Ian and Barbara Good is witnessed by over 20 years of pulling pints here.

THE AXE AND COMPASSES.
Arkesden, nr Saffron Walden. Tel: (01799) 550272

Location: village centre.
Credit cards: Access, Visa.
Bitters: Greene King IPA & Abbot.
Lagers: Kronenbourg, Harp.

Examples of bar meals (lunch & evening, 7 days): *homemade steak & kidney pie; sirloin steak; pork loin on a mushroom & cream sauce topped with stilton; moussaka & garlic bread; moules mariniere; skate; king prawns; cod; plaice; sandwiches; ploughman's.*

Examples of restaurant meals (as above): *roast duck breast; wild venison in brandy redcurrant sauce; chicken, leek & bacon crumble; seafood & game in season; tenderloin of pork with mushroom sauce & stilton; fresh fish dishes; wild mushroom pancake; stir-fry vegetables with mustard sauce in pastry case. Trad. Sun. roasts £10.50 (4 courses).*

NB Children eat at half price.

Newcomers to Arkesden wonder why they've never heard of it before. It is, quite simply, exquisite, and puts many a more famous place to shame. Grand old thatched houses straddle a little stream in the dappled shade of willow trees. For complete perfection a lovely old country pub is required, and that's what you have in 'The Axe and Compasses' - a picturebook 17th-century house, presided over by owner Themis Christou and family. They foster a notably relaxed and unhurried atmosphere, so linger awhile and savour the home cooking; seafood-lovers should note that Tuesday is FISH NIGHT. Star rating in national good pub guide. Children welcome in restaurant and patio areas. Definitely not one to be missed!

THE CROWN
Little Walden, nr Saffron Walden. Tel: (01799) 522475

Location : 1½ miles north of Saffron Walden.
Credit cards : Access, Visa, Mastercard, Eurocard.
Bitters : Boddingtons, Flowers, Bass, Worthington,
ever-changing guests.
Lagers : Stella Artois, Heineken.

Examples of bar meals (lunch & evening, except Sun. evening): *baked mackerel; kidneys turbigo; steak & kidney pie; steaks; chilli; jugged hare with buttered noodles; liver & bacon; escalope of pork cordon bleu; curry; smoked seafood platter; whole plaice; wild mushroom stroganoff; jacket potatoes; daily specials eg skate, mussels in garlic, seafood quiche. Four Sun. roasts plus huge 4-meat combination platter.*

A blend of the new and traditional, the menus are devised in the kitchen of Shaun McAskell, and are chalked daily on a blackboard. Bitters are also changed regularly and served mostly straight from the barrel. The building itself, though, has altered little since it was two 18th-century cottages. The low doors, walk-through fireplaces and timber lattices suggest much older origins, especially in the separate dining room (children welcome). Solid wood furniture, terra cotta and stripped wood floors, plus an old grandfather clock in one corner, all look well here and lend authenticity. Steve and Sue are the young licensees, dispensing good cheer and celebrating red letter days.

THE FARMHOUSE INN

Monk Street, nr Thaxted. Tel: (01371) 830864, Fax: (01371) 831196

Location : 1 mile south of Thaxted off Dunmow Road.
Credit cards : Access, Visa, Amex.
Accommodation : 11 dbls/twins. All en suite, TV, direct phone, tea & coffee, access to fax.
£42.50 per room (£32.50 as sngl); 2 nights for 2 people £75 at
weekends. Tourist Board 3 Crowns.
Bitters : Adnams, Greene King, Wadworth 6X.
Lagers : Carlsberg, Kronenbourg, Carling.

Examples of bar/restaurant meals (lunch & evening, 7 days): *avocado baked with cream cheese & herbs; king prawns wrapped in bacon with lobster sauce; chargrilled steaks; steak & Guinness pie; Essex lamb chops with mint sauce; supreme of chicken stuffed with prawns in mild curry & cream sauce; half roast duck with orange & ginger sauce; game pie; tagliatelle with broccoli, cashew nuts & mushrooms in white wine sauce; potato skins filled with ham & tomato, topped with creamy cheese sauce; potato skins filled with tomato, leeks & basil. Children's menu. Trad. Sun. roasts.*

Why choose a drab, routine motel at which to hold meetings or conferences? Here on a quiet country lane, only 10 - 15 mins from Stansted Airport and the M11, are all the facilities you could want, in a 16th-century farmhouse of character. The only distraction is the nice view over the Chelmer Valley. Food is also distinctly superior, and service more personal. It's probably cheaper, too; even the humble tourist without an expense account will find it affordable, and very handy for Thaxted, one of England's smartest, most historic small towns. Adrian and Lorraine Lloyd have been winning an ever-widening circle of converts in their four years here. Adrian cooks and demonstrates his versatility on monthly Gourmet Nights - Chinese, Italian, Indian, for example. Children are welcome and have play equipment in the garden (with barbecue). The bright and airy dining room serves well for wedding receptions etc.

THE FOX
The Green, Finchingfield. Tel: (01371) 810151

Location: on village green.
Credit cards: Mastercard, Visa, Delta, Switch, Eurocard, JCB, Electron.
Accommodation: 2 dbls/twins (1 en suite). Tea & coffee.
Bitters: Courage Directors, Websters, John Smith, Greene King IPA, 2 guests.
Lagers: Fosters, Carlsberg, Kronenbourg.

Examples from lunch menu (daily): *shepherd's pie; steak & kidney pie; huntsman's pie; lasagne; curry; chilli; scampi; salads; jacket potatoes; ploughman's; sandwiches; daily specials eg chicken & mushroom pie, home-made bread & butter pudding. Trad. Sun. roasts.*

Examples from evening menu (not Suns): *steaks & grills; smuggler's pie; poacher's pie; lamb stew & dumplings; steak & kidney pudding; veg. tikka masala; veg. mornay en croute; Caribbean Wellington. Fresh fish night Fridays. Home-made fruit pies; spotted dick; treacle pud; trifles; fruit salads; gateaux.*

NB: Morning coffee from 9am, afternoon teas. Coach parties welcome by arrangement.

One of England's most depicted villages, idyllic Finchingfield is virtually synonymous with The Fox, a pretty whitewashed coaching inn at the hub of social life for over 500 years. Experienced new licencees (since spring '95) Mike and Anita have no problems filling the newly-opened bedrooms (especially being near Stansted), or indeed the bar and dining area, for they recognise that such a wonderful location is not enough: they must also offer good value. Hence special two-course lunches at £4.95 and 'Two for £10' meals on Monday and Tuesday evenings. Cooking may be described as traditional British; themes include steak & kidney pud evening, St Patrick's Night, Burns' Night etc, but also Beaujolais for a little continental flair. Children very welcome. Small patio to front.

THE WAGGON & HORSES
High Street, Gt Yeldham, nr Halstead. Tel & Fax: (01787) 237936

Location : on A604, 200 yds from famous Yeldham Oak.
Credit cards : Mastercard, Visa, Delta, Switch, Amex, Diners.
Accommodation : 1 sngl, 5 dbls/twins. TV, tea & coffee. c/h. £15pp incl Cont. brkfst.
Rooms are 16th-century.
Bitters : Greene King, 1 regional & 1 national guest.
Lagers : Harp, Kronenbourg.

Examples of bar snacks (lunch & evening, 7 days): *deep-fried potato skins; scampi; plaice (with hand-cut chips); doorstep sandwiches; ploughman's.*

Examples of restaurant meals (as above): *home-made soup; avocado with bacon & tomato salad; steak & kidney pudding; lambs' liver & black back bacon; strips of barbary duck with ginger & honey; chicken breast with creamy mushroom sauce on buttered tagliatelle; 'Joe Blake' sirloin steak. Trad. Sun. roasts £9.95 (3 courses).*

The eye-catching painted waggon to the front was the Rolls Royce of its day; built in 1840, it is one of the oldest in the country. Another outmoded transport is the nearby Colne Valley Steam Railway. Being 'Lovejoy Country' the area has an association with antiques, with many fine buildings, of which this former three 16th-century cottages is one. Two ghosts are said to walk the timbered, split-level bar, one of them a lady who apparently objects to war memorabilia but not the many Punch cartoons with amusing modern 'punch lines'. Young chef Ellie Cox is highly regarded in the area, and her cooking utilises as much fresh and local produce as possible. Landlord (since Nov. 1994) Mike Shiffner, having restored the pub, plans further improvements, including landscaping the garden (which has boules). Games Room has pool, darts and shove ha'penny. Children welcome.

THE VICTORY INN & GINGERBREADS RESTAURANT

The Green, Wickham St Paul's, nr Halstead. Tel: (01787) 269364

Location: on corner of village green by the pond.
Credit cards: Mastercard, Visa, Switch.
Accommodation: 1 sngl (£17.50), 3 dbls/twins (£28). TV, tea & coffee. 2-day break £45pp inc. dinner, b & b.
Bitters: Nethergate, Greene King, Adnams, Websters, guest.
Lagers: Fosters, Kronenbourg, Carlsberg, Eichbaum LA.

Examples of bar/restaurant meals (lunch & evening, 7 days): *egg & prawn mornay; curry; roast beef; steaks & grills; chicken Leoni; grilled whole lemon sole; vegetable chilli; salads; sandwiches.; daily specials eg home-made steak & kidney pudding, local pheasant in madeira sauce with mushrooms & bacon, chicken & pineapple with light spicy sauce & Malibu, h/m Yorkshire puds. Banoffi pie on shortbread base (speciality); toffee apple & pecan pie; ginger sponge & lemon sauce.*

Built around 1700, this family-run freehouse is still known locally as The Wickham Ship, although the nearest body of water is the swimming pool in the garden, for use of guests. The large open-plan bar is warm and cosy, with open fire, low beams and tranquil views over the vast village green, one of the county's finest, as has the smart adjoining restaurant (available for functions up to 50). One is well based here for outings to Hedingham Castle, Colne Valley Railway, Lavenham and Constable Country, but be back in time to enjoy the fruits of chefs Alex Newman's and Sylvi Cook's labour. Landlady Pam Bush is also an experienced cook; since 1990 she and husband Keith have made theirs one of the best liked inns of these parts. Children welcome; play area and barbecue. Darts, pool and dominoes.

THE GREEN MAN
Gosfield, nr Halstead. Tel: (01787) 472746

Location : on Braintree to Hedingham road.
Credit Cards : Access, Visa.
Bitters : Greene King.
Lagers : Kronenbourg.

Examples of bar meals (lunchtime 7 days, every evening except Sunday): *Evenings: game soup with sherry; breaded mushrooms with garlic butter; Dover sole; oxtail ragout; steaks; boiled beef & carrots; roast duck with orange sauce; plaice fillets with prawn sauce; steak & kidney pudding; selection of home-made fresh vegetarian dishes (eg spinach pancakes, vegetable lasagne). Lunchtime: Cold buffet; hot dish of the day. Choice of desserts.*

'Essex Dining Pub of the Year 1995' is the latest accolade from a leading national good pub guide for the best traditional food in the county. Nothing is frozen; all is cooked to order - special requests catered for if possible. You may not be able to resist the succulent array of cooked meats, shellfish, salmon and more on the buffet table, and speciality evenings - eg Italian, Greek, Curry, Fish - are also very popular, so booking is advised. It's refreshing to see staff so well turned-out, courteous and hard-working. Tellingly, most have worked for proprietor John Arnold for many years, including his 'right-hand lady', Janet Harrington, now in her 25th year here. It is these 'old-fashioned' virtues which endow this 16th-century pub with uncommon warmth and civility. Children are tolerated if well behaved; if not there's a rather nice garden by the large car park. Small room for private functions.

THE GREEN DRAGON

Upper London Road, Young's End, nr Braintree. Tel: (01245) 361030, Fax: (01245) 362575

Location : A131 2 miles south of Braintree - nr Essex showground.
Credit cards : Visa, Mastercard, Diners, Amex.
Bitters : Greene King Abbot & IPA. Bottled selection.
Lagers : Harp, Kronenbourg.

Examples of bar meals (lunch & evening, 7 days): *homemade pies; Suffolk hotpot; steaks; veal in mustard sauce; smoked salmon & prawn risotto; fresh fish & shellfish daily; trad. roasts; Indian-style chicken; fillet of salmon en croute; leek, mushroom & potato cakes; chicken & bacon parcels; vegetarian specials; daily blackboard specials.*

Examples of restaurant meals (as above): *sea bass roasted with prawn & leek sauce; skate wings pan-fried with capers; Bradon rost (hot smoked fillet salmon with whisky sauce); turkey Alexander; roast duckling with Cointreau sauce; chicken Wellington; beefsteak, kidney & mushroom pie; kleftiko; steaks; brown rice & hazelnut loaf. Trad. Sun. roasts.*

Bob and Mandy Greybrook have been at the Green Dragon for over 10 years, during which time it has become one of the most popular pubs in the area (the large car park is a necessity) and the recipient of numerous catering awards. Fresh seafood - langoustines and salmon from Scotland, oysters and wetfish from nearby Mersea - has increasingly become a speciality. The 48-seater restaurant was converted from a barn, serving a la carte and fixed-price menus, plus a Sunday roast menu throughout the day - bookings always advised. Or just drop by for a meal in the cosy bar or snug. The garden has a play area with aviary. Private parties and weddings catered for.

THE GREEN MAN

Howe Street, nr Chelmsford. Tel: (01245) 360203

Photo courtesy Priory Photographic of Chelmsford

Location: on main road, north side of village.
Credit cards: Mastercard, Visa, Switch, Eurocard, Delta.
Bitters: Ridleys, John Smith's.
Lagers: Carlsberg, Fosters, Holsten Export.

Examples of bar meals (lunch & evening except Mon. lunch in winter): *garlic mushroom hotpot; smoked haddock with poached egg; fresh battered cod; home-cooked ham; h/m steak & kidney pie; liver, bacon & onions; steaks; lamb chops with mint sauce; jacket potatoes; ploughman's; sandwiches; daily specials eg chicken in stilton & broccoli sauce, half roast duck in orange sauce, sausage & beef hotpot, fresh whole plaice. H/m apple pie; treacle tart; mandarin cheesecake; chocolate roulade; lemon brulée. Children's menu. Trad. Sun. roasts.*

NB: closed Monday lunchtimes in winter.

"The oldest pub in Essex" - parts of it date from the 14th century - stands in five acres by the River Chelmer, with fishing rights, and in good walking and cycling country. But it is another outdoor pursuit, horseracing, which is evidently an interest of ex-farmer Richard Bailey, a local man who 'took up the reins' as new landlord on July 4th, 1995. His cousin Kim is a professional trainer, and you could join a syndicate to buy and maintain a horse. Other innovations are in the pipeline, including live jazz (with special menus) on the first Monday of each month and a room for children. They will also approve of the play area and aviary in the garden. One young lad apparently likes it here so much that his spirit is reluctant to leave! Once ensconced in the warm, cosy, timbered dining room or lounge, warmed by an open log fire, and after a good 'farmhouse-size' home-cooked meal, you may feel the same. Weddings and private functions welcome.

77

THE BEEHIVE

High Street, Gt Waltham, nr Chelmsford. Tel: (01245) 360356

Location : village centre, opposite church.
Credit cards : Mastercard, Visa.
Bitters : Ridleys Rumpus & IPA, John Smith's, guest.
Lagers : Carlsberg Export, Fosters.

Examples of bar meals (lunch & evening, 7 days): *home-made soups; king prawns with dips; mussels in white wine & garlic; vegetable samosas; steak & kidney pie; medallions of pork in cider sauce; butter grilled halibut steak 'landlord style'; deep-fried plaice; home-cooked ham. Home-made treacle tart; jam sponge; lemon cream pie; chocolate fudge cake. Trad. Sun. roasts.*

It's not always easy to strike a balance between being a homely locals' pub and appealing to a wider audience interested in good home-made food at reasonable prices, but The Beehive manages it with aplomb. Landlord Mike Smail is an experienced chef, and with wife Jan he came to this pleasant village in October '95, having previously run Chelmsford Golf Club. Daughter Debbie is star of the Public Bar, where other attractions are pool and darts, plus quiz nights on Thursdays. Monthly gourmet and theme nights are planned for the quite separate lounge/dining area. There has been a pub of this name on the site for centuries, and although this one dates only from the 1950's, it has acquired its ghostly apparitions: a mysterious grey cat and a hand which gropes through a wall! It stands by the Essex Way footpath, and there are also lovely walks through the parkland of the Langley Estate, just opposite. Ask about the over-60's discount card, usable Mon. - Fri.

THE SHIP
Stock Road, West Hanningfield. Tel: (01277) 840201

Location : on B1007 1/2 mile north of Stock (2 mins off A12).
Credit cards : pending.
Bitters : Flowers Original & IPA, Tetley.
Lagers : Carlsberg, Stella Artois.

Examples of bar/dining room meals (lunch & evening, 7 days): *deep-fried brie in h/m batter with cranberry sauce; steaks & grills; lamb valentine; pork fillet with stilton; breast of chicken supreme; American rib; baked local trout; poached halibut steak; provencale nut Wellington; liver, bacon & fried onions; lasagne; omelettes; salads; jacket potatoes; sandwiches; daily specials eg steak & mushroom pie, h/m Cornish pastie, grilled wing of skate. Fresh fish specials Thursday evenings. Home-made desserts. Trad. Sun. roasts (booking advised).*

Stock is a pleasant village but with more than its fair share of pubs, so having prospered over the past five years Terry and Maureen Clifford are obviously doing something right, and it's not hard to fathom: food is almost entirely home-made, plates are full and prices very competitive. Built using ships' timbers in 1565 and cheered by an open fire, the pub itself is conducive to a good atmosphere. Sunday evenings are especially lively, when bingo and a quiz raise a laugh and substantial proceeds to local charities. Star footballers from a well known Premier League London club (with which Terry has close connections) are regulars. Red letter days are popular (especially Mother's Day), as are theme nights like Pie & Mash. Children are welcome, and the large, attractive garden has play equipment, plus a barbecue and outside bar - ideal for weddings etc. Darts and shoveha'penny. West Hanningfield Reservoir (famous for trout) very near.

THE HURDLE MAKERS ARMS

Post Office Road, Woodham Mortimer, nr Maldon. Tel: (01245) 225169

Location : off the A414 between Danbury & Maldon.
Credit cards : not accepted.
Bitters : Greene King IPA & Abbott.
Lagers : Heineken, Tennents Extra, Red Stripe, Stella Artois.

Examples of bar meals (lunchtimes only, 7 days): *lasagne; grilled gammon; ham off the bone; homemade steak kidney & mushroom pie; Mediterranean prawn salad; various fillings in rolls & sandwiches; ploughmans; Devon smoked prawns; curries; smoked chicken; grilled lemon sole. Homemade fruit pie.*

A former winner of CAMRA Pub of the Year, The Hurdle Makers has a name and style all its own. It is set in two acres of well tended garden, wherein is a children's play area - there's also a family room. Such a garden readily accommodates regular barbecues, at which up to 200 can sit under 'sunbrellas', or into a marquee if necessary. There's also a pitch-and-putt driving range to the rear, and the pub has its own golf society. The menu above, though typical, changes weekly. The food is totally fresh and never fried; Terry and Sue Green take pride in that, and also advise customers that no bookings are taken, just arrive. Inside you'll find two lovely oak-beamed bars with flagstone floors, settles dotted round tables and an open fire. All the washrooms are immaculate, and the disabled have their own. Pub bar has darts, dominoes and shut-the-box.

THE Du CANE ARMS

The Village, Gt Braxted, nr Witham. Tel: (01621) 891697

Location : village centre.
Credit cards : Mastercard, Visa, Delta.
Bitters : Greene King IPA, Courage Best, Websters, John Smith, guest.
Lagers : Carlsberg, Fosters, Holsten.

Examples of bar meals (lunch & evening, 7 days): *home-made steak, kidney & mushroom pie; beef midani; chicken princess; lasagne; steaks; trout; caprisciosa fettucini (seafood); salads; sandwiches. Home-made fruit crumbles; treacle pud; spotted dick; chocolate pud; gateaux.*

Examples of restaurant meals (as above): *smoked eel smetana; mushroom bourgignon; beef stroganoff; ragout of scallops & crayfish; salmon parcel; breast of duckling oriental style; steak midani; vegetable midani (midanis a speciality). Trad. Sun. roasts.*

NB: Bar meals may be enjoyed in restaurant on weekdays for a £1 cover charge.

Fresh herbs from the garden, fresh-baked rolls from the oven, interesting and predominantly home-made food (the uncommon midani dishes are particularly popular): The Du Cane Arms is drawing custom from a wide radius to this out-of-the-way village. The Hyde family - Eric and Brenda, Alan and Angela - came here in spring 1991 with many years of experience. Their high standards refreshingly extend to a ban on foul language. There has been an inn on the site since 16th century, when the Du Canes were the local gentry, but this one dates from the 1930's, and is light and airy, with pot plants in the L-shaped bar, fresh flowers in the restaurant (which also serves for functions up to 30). Children welcome. Small garden. Pottery opposite, Braxted Hall and golf course nearby.

81

THE BLACK BUOY

Black Buoy Hill, off East Street, Wivenhoe. Tel: (01206) 822425, Fax: (01206) 825587

Location : B1028 to end of village, turn left past church.
Credit cards : not accepted.
Bitters : Flowers Original & IPA, guest.
Lagers : Stella Artois, Carlsberg.

Examples from lunch menu (daily): *smoked prawns with garlic mayonnaise; Vietnamese-style chicken; baked red mullet with anchovy butter; pork steak braised in cider; seafood Florentine; steaks; home-made burgers; late breakfast; ploughman's; sandwiches. Belgian white chocolate ice cream; apricot & macaroon parfait; apricot bread & butter pudding; damson & apple pie; treacle tart. Trad. Sun. roasts.*

Examples from evening menu (not Suns or Mons): *range of home-made Balti dishes with home-made naan (renowned); roasted Mediterranean vegetables pasta; salmon & crab filo parcels; lamb noisettes with olives; chargrilled specialities incl. Cajun chicken; jacket potatoes with unusual fillings (award-winning). Theme evenings, eg Fish.*

Wivenhoe is one of East Anglia's most unsung treasures, a wonderful 'find' for the first-time visitor. Its narrow streets and riverside cottages are so redolent of a Cornish fishing village, yet it lies in secrecy barely three miles from Colchester. It is further blessed by this little gem of a pub, formerly three 16th-century cottages, fittingly decorated in a nautical theme. Warm, traditional and unpretentious, its appeal is classless; a high bench by the window is the favourite perch of local drinkers. Open fires, mulled wine and mince pies will drive out the worst winter chill, and aficionados of Far Eastern cookery will drool over the celebrated Balti and other dishes - chef proprietor Richard Blackwell is a specialist, and blends and grinds his own spices. Children welcome if dining. Small patio and car park.

*What is the brass cooking utensil
in the restaurant window?*

THE TENDRING TAVERN

Heath Road, Tendring. Tel: (01255) 870262

Location : 1½ miles north of Tendring village on B1035.
Credit cards : Mastercard, Access, Visa.
Bitters : Greene King, Flowers.
Lagers : Stella Artois, Carlsberg.

Examples of bar/restaurant meals (lunch & evening except Sun. evenings): *mini spring rolls with oriental sauce; tiger prawns in garlic butter; Spanish paella; Portuguese cataplana (seasonal fish & shellfish in rich wine & tomato sauce); chicken with black bean sauce; chicken piri-piri; steak & kidney pie; beef stroganoff; steaks; vegetable curry; deep-fried vegetable fritters with spicy dip & fried rice; ploughman's; sandwiches; jacket potatoes; daily specials eg pasta Florentine with ham, cod & chips, prawns in herb batter, Thai chicken curry, Bangkok prawns, balti chicken. Steamed sponge pudding; treacle tart; apple pie; toffee, apple & pecan pie; sherry trifle. Children's menu. Trad. Sun. roasts £4.95.*

Landlady Margaret Trotter is highly skilled in the art of Chinese cusine, in fact probably more so than many a Chinese chef, thanks to long years spent in Hong Kong and the Far East. She and husband Frank present traditional British favourites and some unusual European dishes, too. Choice is further enhanced by occasional theme evenings, such as Thai or Greek. More attractive inside than out, their Victorian pub houses a number of curios, including a collection of old sewing machines, shoe horns, scales, and basketry hanging from the ceiling. A pleasant little conservatory overlooks the garden, in which there is children's play equipment. Circular rota pool and darts. T-shirts for sale. Beth Chatto's Garden, Constable Country and the coast all nearby.

THE ANGEL INN

Stoke by Nayland, nr Colchester. Tel: (01206) 263245, Fax: (01206) 263373

Location : village centre.
Credit cards : Access, Amex, Diners, Visa.
Accommodation : 6 doubles. All en suite, TV, phone, hair dryer, tea & coffee. £57.50 per room incl. (£44 as sngl).
Bitters : Adnams, Greene King.
Lagers : Carlsberg, Kronenbourg.

Examples from lunch & supper menu (served daily in bar & Well Room, where table may be booked): *fresh dressed crab; home-made fishcakes; tomato & feta cheese salad; wild boar sausages; steak & kidney pudding; honey-glazed roast rack of lamb; sauté of liver & bacon; griddled fresh wing of skate; steamed fillets of salmon & halibut; roast ballantine of duckling. Apple, apricot & sultana jalousse; raspberry & vanilla bavarois; warm sticky toffee pudding. Trad. Sun. roasts. All is freshly prepared on the premises.*

Celebrating 10 phenomenally successful years under current ownership, widely admired and feted by the leading guides, this is one of the region's best known establishments. Recent accolades are Egon Ronay's Pub Accommodation of the Year Award 1995 (for the whole country), and Suffolk Dining Pub of the Year in a major good food guide. Although the Georgian facade is attractive enough, it is but a prelude to the very splendid 17th-century interior. Looking for the most outstanding feature, one would settle on the gallery which leads from the tastefully appointed bedrooms to a view over the restaurant. A charming little lounge divides the bars from the two dining rooms, one of which has an ancient 40' well. The village is a very pretty one, in the heart of Constable Country and just 15 minutes drive from Colchester.

THE PLOUGH INN

Brockley Green, nr Hundon, nr Clare. Tel: (01440) 786789, Fax: (01440) 786710

Location : 1½ miles from Hundon towards Kedington. If in doubt, phone.
Credit cards : Access, Visa.
Accommodation : 7 twins/dbls, 1 family. All en suite, teletext TV, phone, hair dryer, trouser press, tea & coffee. Weekend breaks £175 for 2 people, 2 nights dinner, B & B. ETB 4-Crown. Member of Logis. Caravan Club certified location.
Bitters : local traditional ales, weekly guest.
Lagers : rotating premier & standard.

Examples of bar meals (lunch & evening from 6pm, 7 days): *home-made soups; beef & Guinness pie; fresh fish; steaks; ploughmans.*

Examples of restaurant meals (as above): *lemon sole with prawns; duckling breast with orange; steaks; salmon poached in wine & cream; vegetarian dishes; seafood night every Tuesday. Trad. Sun. roasts (booking advised).*

For over 30 years The Plough has been in the hands of the Rowlinson family. Now in their 14th year here, David and Marion are ably assisted by Jim and Margaret Forbes. Soft red bricks and oak beams from an old barn engender a country pub atmosphere. Whilst providing modern amenities (the restaurant is plush and air conditioned, for example) it is without sacrifice of old fashioned friendliness and charm. This and good home cooked food (seafood a speciality) has won a place in local affections and a number of major guides. A pianist accompanies Friday dinner, and theme evenings and tutored wine evenings are currently planned. Not an easy one to find, but patience reaps its rewards. The views alone, over the rolling countryside, are worth the effort, and there is also a south-facing landscaped terrace garden. Well placed to reach Cambridge, Bury St Edmunds and Lavenham. Children welcome.

THE PLOUGH

The Green, Rede, nr Bury St. Edmunds. Tel. (01284) 789208

Location : cul de sac, not far from church.
Credit cards : Access, Visa.
Bitters : Greene King.
Lagers : Harp, Kronenbourg.

Examples of bar meals (lunchtime every day, & evenings except Sunday): *fresh fish (speciality); steaks; curries; salads; daily specials eg jugged hare in port & wine sauce; romany lamb with spaghetti & parmesan cheese; beef in horseradish sauce; chicken, ham & stilton crumble.*

Examples of restaurant meals (evenings only, not Sundays. Traditional Sunday lunch): *pigeon breasts in Madeira & spinach; venison; trout; roast duck; veal in Dijon mustard & brandy; poached salmon; local game (speciality).*

In a quiet cul de sac by the village pond, pretty as a picture (inside and out), here is the very essence of the inimitable English country pub, built around 1610 on the highest point in Suffolk. The inglenook fireplace is an especially handsome one, the beams look good for another 500 years, and the fine collection of teapots strikes the right note without lapsing into tweeness. Amiable hosts Brian and Joyce Desborough and staff foster an unstuffy, unhurried atmosphere, but in summer you may prefer the large sunny garden with a tropical aviary, a dovecote and ponies - children love it! They are welcome inside in the eating areas. The separate restaurant has a good name (portions are substantial), and the Plough is a regular in national guides.

THE GEORGE & DRAGON

Hall Street, Long Melford. Tel: (01787) 371285

Location : centre of village, on main road.
Credit cards : Access, Visa, Mastercard.
Accommodation : 2 sngls, 4 dbls/twins, 1 family. All en suite, TV, direct phone. Special
                breaks by arrangement.
Bitters : Greene King, guest.
Lagers : Kronenbourg, Castlemaine.

Examples of bar/restaurant meals (lunch & evening, 7 days): *melon & prawn fan served on fruit sauce; game terrine. Swordfish steak on fresh lime sauce; halibut with white grapes in Muscadet sauce; roundels of lamb with hot mint sauce; pork & apple pie; kidney bordelaise; beef in Abbot ale; Suffolk sausages with onion gravy; smoked chicken with pasta; steaks; vegetarian dishes; sandwiches; daily specials. Desserts.*

*N*B Open all day except Sundays.

"Not a pub, not a restaurant, but a true village inn" - the words of Peter, Marilyn and Ian Thorogood, who've revived the art of innkeeping at their 16th-century coaching inn over the past 10 years. That means "no karaoke, discos, keg beer or men in over-sized suits drinking from bottles!" Instead, you have delicious and filling meals created in the kitchen from fine local produce, traditional local beers and superb French wines (clarets especially good). Entertainment, too, is traditional, with live music every Wednesday. Look out, too, for special commemorative dinners - St George's Day, for example. Well-behaved children are welcome, and there is a garden. An ideal base to stay; right in the heart of the region, Long Melford is England's longest village, a Mecca for antique collectors, and boasts two Tudor Halls and Suffolk's finest church. Recommended by most major pub guides.

THE BEAGLE

Old Hadleigh Road, Sproughton, nr Ipswich. Tel: (01473) 730455

Location : Cul de sac next to new road, near Constable Country Hotel.
Credit cards : Acces, Visa, Switch.
Bitters : Constantly rotate eg Bass, Hancocks, Old Speckled Hen, Stones,
Worthington, Greene King Abbott.
Lagers : Staropramen, Carling.

Examples of bar meals (ALL DAY & EVERY DAY): *filled potato skins; steak & ale pie; chicken, ham & mushroom pie; hearty vegetable pie; fish & chips; chicken in barbecue sauce with bacon & cheese; liver, bacon & onions; seafood salad; Yorkshire pudding with sausages in onion gravy; steaks & grills; spinach & brie tart; ploughman's; sandwiches; daily specials eg baked haddock in wild mushroom sauce, brie & courgette crumble, roast duck & blackcurrants, beef stew & dumplings. School pudding; chilled sticky toffee cake; treacle tart. Trad. Sun. roasts.*

Readers who know of John and Barbara Taylor from their 13 years at The Robin Hood, Clacton, will be pleased to know that the skills which regularly won accolades from Egon Ronay and other major guides have been transferred to this beautifully restored and extended country pub, formerly four cottages. It is an example of how it should be done, without the ghastly Disneyland excesses of some designers. Cooking is also traditionally British and served in belt-loosening portions, yet at reasonable prices. You may even dine on the house if you win the free prize draw. Exceptionally good value bin ends are chalked on a blackboard. Children welcome if eating, and the garden has a play area.

THE COMPASSES INN
Ipswich Road, Holbrook. Tel: (01473) 328332, Fax: (01473) 327403

Location: on main road in village centre.
Credit cards: Access, Visa, Diners, Amex.
Bitters: Benskins, Tetley, guest.
Lagers: Stella Artois, Carlsberg.

Examples of bar/restaurant meals (lunch & evening, 7 days): *kleftico; steaks; seafood & traditional lasagne; kidney turbigo; chicken curry; lemon chicken; homemade pies; fresh fish daily; daily roast and many more, incl. large vegetarian selection.*

Travellers once hired ponies here for the journey to Ipswich, which was a safer mode of transport than by boat on the River Orwell, to judge from the engraved ships' timbers dredged up and put on display. Also on display, hanging from the beams, are more than 1000 key fobs. Recent refurbishment has resulted in a more open-plan and spacious interior. Tables may be reserved in the light and airy dining area, but the stress is always on informality. However, what really makes the Compasses so popular are the generous portions of good food at very reasonable prices. Children are allowed and have a play area outside; grown-ups can relax in the garden or on the patio. In the same hands for over 15 years, the pub features regularly in national guides.

BUTT AND OYSTER

Pin Mill, Chelmondiston, nr Ipswich. Tel: (01473) 780764

Location : off B1456 Shotley Road.
Credit Cards : not accepted.
Bitters : Tolly Cobbold - on handpump or from barrel, from the reborn brewery across the river. Occasional guests.
Lagers : Stella Artois, Carlsberg.
Extended Hours : Winter: Mon-Fri 11am-3pm, 7pm-11pm. Sun 12 noon-3pm, 7pm-10:30pm.
Summer : Mon-Fri 11am-11pm. Sunday as winter. SATURDAYS 11am to 11pm ALL YEAR.

Examples of bar meals (lunch & evening, 7 days): *fishermans pie; smoked chicken with onion & chive dip; savoury sausage pie; pork & apple pie; steak & kidney pie; tiger tail prawns; seafood platter; crispy curry pancakes; honey roast half duck; farm manager's lunch; ravioli. Limited menus (rolls etc) outside main hours.*

Views of the River Orwell such as this are a major asset. However, not content to rest on nature's laurels, Dick and Brenda Mainwaring really work at keeping the Butt and Oyster authentic. The concept works, as national guides and newspapers testify, and CAMRA named this the 'Regional Pub of the Year 1993.' The locals also treasure it, and the elders will confirm that it is unchanged over 60 years. Even the pub games, some almost forgotten elsewhere, live on here; juke boxes and the like do not. The view from the bar and dining room overlooks the boats and river, and at very high tides the river nearly overlooks them. There's an old smoke room with bare floorboards and smoke-stained ceiling. The homecooked food varies daily and is of generous proportions. There's a children's room, or sit at tables by the river's edge.

THE RAMSHOLT ARMS
Dock Road, Ramsholt, nr Woodbridge. Tel: (01394) 411229

Location: off B1083 Woodbridge-Bawdsey road.
Credit cards: Access, Visa.
Accommodation: 1 double, 3 twin (1 with private facilities); TV on request; £25 pp
b & b; Special weekend rates.
Bitters: Adnams, guests.
Lagers: Heineken, Stella Artois. Good selection of bottled beers & lagers.

Examples of bar/restaurant meals (lunch & evening, 7 days; extended hours in summer): *large bowl of mussels steamed in white wine & garlic; salad of breast of woodcock with mushrooms; Scotch smoked salmon; prawn & brie filo parcels; fillet of fresh halibut in lemon butter; local partridge pot-roasted in red wine & onion sauce; 12oz sirloin steak pan-fried; spinach & cream cheese crepes. H/m chocolate mousse; profiteroles; sticky toffee pudding; fresh fruit meringues & sorbets. Trad. Sun. roasts.*

No photograph can really do justice to one of East Anglia's finest riverside pubs, right on the beach by the old barge quay at Ramsholt. A former shooting lodge and smugglers' inn, where beer was poured into enamel jugs and the lighting provided by paraffin lamps, it enjoys a very special location in beautiful, remote countryside. Nowadays it is known for high quality and beautifully presented home-cooked food, using local produce (especially fish and game) to the full on a daily-changing menu. After as warm a welcome as one would wish for, relax in front of the open fire, sampling the fine ales, whilst taking in the spectacular views in both directions over the River Deben, with its abundant birdlife (some quite rare). There's a separate dining room and bar with river-fronting terrace. Ample parking.

Who was the lady who shared a drink with Nelson here?

THE ADMIRAL'S HEAD

Sandy Lane, Little Bealings, nr Woodbridge. Tel: (01473) 625912

Location: from Ipswich, turn left off old A12 just before Police HQ; from Martlesham roundabout take A1214 towards Ipswich for 500yds, turn right.

Credit cards: Access, Visa.

Bitters: Bealings Own Brand, Adnams, Flowers, Courage, weekly guests.

Lagers: Stella Artois, Heineken, Kronenbourg, Fosters.

Examples of bar meals (lunch & evening, 7 days): *hot & cold buffets; hot smoked mackerel with orange sauce; bouillabaise; kleftico; grilled skate with lemon & herb butter; beef stroganoff; chicken Kiev; rack of lamb; roast duck; minute steak chasseur. Bread & butter pudding & selection of home-made sweets. Four Sun. roasts plus four-meat combination platter.*

Nelson is the eponymous admiral, and the story goes that he met a lady here on occasion. The facade is contemporary of that period, but it is immediately obvious that the timbered interior preceded him by two centuries. Shielded behind a lattice, the gallery is the most favoured area in which to sit, although the terrace may be preferred in summer. Of special interest in the pleasant little dining room to the rear (available for private funtions, seating 48) is an old well, from which water was drawn until quite recently. Good food and ale at fair prices mean that the pub is well known locally, but newcomers may have to search a little for this tiny hamlet. Children welcome.

THE WHITE HORSE

The Street, Easton, nr Woodbridge. Tel: (01728) 746456

Location : village centre, near church.
Credit cards : Mastercard, Eurocard, Visa, Delta, Switch.
Bitters : Tolly Cobbold, Flowers.
Lagers : Carlsberg, Carlsberg Export.

Examples of bar meals (lunch & evening, 7 days): *king prawns in garlic butter; fillet steak with stilton in red wine sauce; fillet of pork in cream & mustard sauce; lamb curry; stir-fry chicken in garlic butter; chilli; chargrilled steaks; fresh fish daily; leek, stilton & potato bake; baguettes. Trad. Sun. roasts.*

As pretty an example of a true Suffolk pub as one could ask for, this 16th-century cottage will not disappoint. Inside it is warm and homely, with flint walls, pine tables and a two-tier dining room divided by a timber lattice. The atmosphere is easy and hospitable, but even were it not so the landlady's home cooking would be reason enough for a visit. Chalked daily on a blackboard, the menu will suit every taste, without resort to a freezer, and at reasonable prices. A guitarist performs on occasion. A small function room also houses a pool table and dartboard. The village itself is very pleasant (distinguished by the Crinkly-Crankly Wall), with many fine walks and Easton Farm Park nearby. Family room; play area in garden.

YE OLD CROSS KEYS
Crabbe Street, Aldeburgh. Tel: (01728) 452637

Location: seafront, by lifeboat.
Credit cards: not accepted.
Bitters: Adnams.
Lagers: Lowenbrau, Carling, Castlemaine. James White cider.

Examples of bar meals (lunch & evening, 7 days): *homemade steak & kidney pie/pud; soups; lamb hotpot; authentic curries; fisherman's pie; seafood pancakes, oysters, lobster, crab, salmon, ploughman's. Jam roly-poly (noted); summer pudding.*

Aldeburgh is one of the prettiest seaside towns on the east coast, and is of course famed for its music festival in June. Another very good reason to visit is this super little 16th-century pub, tucked away between the main street and sea front. It looks every inch the fisherman's haunt it once was, and the nautical flavour extends to the home cooked meals, local seafood being the speciality. Graham and Penny Prior upgraded levels of comfort some years ago when they took over, without losing the spirit of the place. The solid inglenook, dividing the bar into two, remains the centre piece. To the rear is a bright, clean food bar which leads out to a small sheltered garden (children permitted) with plenty of tables and chairs and views out to sea. A devout local following makes it advisable to arrive early in summer. Rated by Les Routiers and other national guides. Large car park nearby.

THE FALCON INN

Earl Soham, nr Framlingham. Tel: (01728) 685263

Location: village centre (country setting), on A1120.
Credit cards: not accepted.
Accommodation: 4 rooms (2 en suite), BTB & Brittany Ferries approved. From £19 pp incl.
Bitters: Greene King Abbot & IPA.
Lagers: Kronenbourg, Harp.

Examples of bar meals (lunch & evening, 7 days. Limited menu Sunday lunchtime, due to popularity of 3-course lunch at £6.95 approx): *steak & kidney pie (featured in local paper); home cooked gammon; curries; ploughmans. Separate vegetarian menu.*

Examples of restaurant meals (evenings only, Mon - Sat): *venison in red wine; rump steak (noted); beef bourgignon; chicken Kiev; vegetarian choices.*

NB Morning coffee and homemade scones.

From the smart bedrooms you can gaze out over a bowling green and the open fields of Earl Soham, previous winner of the "Best Kept Village" award. After a hearty breakfast, you are well placed to tour Framlingham Castle, Dunwich, Southwold and nearby animal and bird sanctuaries. Paul and Lavina Algar and staff have for many years been extending a warm welcome to vistors to their well preserved 15th-century free house, replete with ancient timbers, log fire and other period features. In summer the large garden is a sunny spot for lunch, and children are welcome any time in the pleasant restaurant, with crisp linen and flowers on every table. Food is mostly all homecooked. If you are touring further afield, this being the heart of East Anglia, Sandringham is only 90 mins, and Constable Country just one hour. Functions catered for. Coaches by apptmnt.

THE TROWEL & HAMMER INN

Mill Road, Cotton, nr Stowmarket. Tel: (01499) 781234, Fax: (01499) 781765

Location : east side of village; from Stowmarket turn right off B1113 at signpost.
Credit cards : Access, Visa, Mastercard, Eurocard, Delta, Switch, JCB.
Bitters : Adnams, Greene King, Nethergate, guest.
Lagers : Kronenbourg, Carlsberg.

Examples of bar meals (lunch & evening, 7 days): *filos of brie with creamy chive sauce; grilled sardines with herb butter; avocado salad with chicken & prawns; crab & herb pancakes; liver & bacon with onion gravy; fresh deep-fried cod with chips; steaks; kleftico; creamy leek, potato & stilton pie; steak, kidney & ale pie; ploughman's.*

Examples of restaurant meals (restaurant closed Sun. evenings & Mons): *terrine of salmon with watercress & dill; èscalope of salmon with spinach & hollandaise sauce; confit of duck perigordin; fillet steak en croute. Pancakes with blackcurrants & cassis; chocolate & Cointreau mousse in brandy snap. Trad. Sun. roasts.*

This 15th-century freehouse, one of the best known and most picturesque in the region, was acquired in May '95 by Simon Piers-Hall (formerly of the wine trade) and Julie Huff (formerly of the celebrated Royal Oak, Yattendon). It is gratifying enough that it should continue as a family concern, but they have also introduced exciting menus, always freshly prepared despite their broad scope and daily revision, and accompanied by an outstanding wine list. In winter lovely open fires broadcast good cheer; in summer you may prefer to splash in the swimming pool in the large garden. There's also indoor pool - the kind played on a flat table. The cosy oak-beamed restaurant is well suited to private parties, and there's occasional live music. Well-behaved children welcome.

THE SWAN
Hoxne, nr Eye. Tel: (01379) 668275, Fax: (01379) 668168

Location: village centre.
Credit Cards: Visa, Mastercard.
Bitters: Adnams, Greene King Abbott, Tetleys, Kilkenny.
Lagers: Carlsberg, Lowenbrau, Labatt.

Examples of bar meals (lunch & evening Mon - Fri, plus Sat lunch, plus trad Sun lunch in winter, cold buffet in summer): *homemade soups; haddock & prawn gratinee; pancake mushrooms & cheese; wild boar steak with red cabbage; Lancashire hotpot; baked stuffed avocado; sandwiches.*

Examples from dining room menu (Sat. evenings only): *herby brie parcels; roast partridge with braised red cabbage & chestnuts; scampi provencale; lamb cutlets in herby breadcrumbs; vegetarian by request. Sticky toffee pudding; chocolate pot; bread & butter pudding; apple & calvados pancake.*

Time has marched slowly through the village of Hoxne (pronounced 'Hoxon'), and nowhere has it trod more softly than The Swan. Oak floors and beams, huge inglenooks - words barely do justice to the superb 15th-century interior, cosy and comfortable, lovingly preserved by Frances and Tony Thornton-Jones. Their careful refurbishment of this former coaching inn provides an exemplary blend of improvement without ruination. The honourable tradition regarding food is still observed; good and fresh and at very reasonable prices - from a bowl of soup to a three-course meal. There's a games room with pool and shove ha'penny, and a croquet lawn in the garden. Well behaved children welcome. Enthusiastically recommended by Anglia TV's Food Programme, national guides and local people!

THE BLACK HORSE INN & STABLES RESTAURANT

The Street, Thorndon, nr Eye. Tel & Fax: (01379) 678523

Location : 2 miles off A140 Norwich to Ipswich road at Stoke Ash.
Credit cards : Access, Visa.
Bitters : Greene King Abbot & IPA, Woodfordes Wherry, guest.
Lagers : Kronenbourg, Carlsberg, Castlemaine.

Examples of bar/restaurant meals (lunch & evening, 7 days): *steaks & grills; curry; chilli; lasagne; pasta shells with cheese & garlic sauce; steak & kidney pie; scampi; plaice; mushroom stroganoff with cream & brandy; jacket potatoes; salads; sandwiches; many daily specials eg deep-fried brie, crispy coated vegetables with garlic & mayonnaise dip, wild boar casserole, pork & apple with cider & cream, venison casserole with port & cranberry (speciality), halibut steak with white wine & herb sauce. Many homemade desserts. Children's menu. Trad. Sun. roasts £7.75 (3 courses).*

This 16th-century freehouse (run for several years now by Rod and Julia Waldron, members of The Guild of Master Craftsmen) has one of the most extensive and innovative menus in the area. In addition to the time-honoured favourites, a long list of home-cooked daily specials is chalked on a daily blackboard. Jacket potatoes (with low fat margarine, if requested) are always available as a healthy alternative to fries. The restaurant has been cleverly converted from actual stables, and the stalls are singularly conducive to intimacy and good conversation. In a friendly atmosphere, a warm welcome is extended by the staff, families included. Children like to peer down the 42' well (covered by plate glass!) in the heavily timbered bar, and there's a lawned garden with seating. Occasional Morris dancing and Pony and Trap meets. Beers fresh and well kept.

THE WHITE HORSE

Badingham, nr Framlingham. Tel: (01728) 638280

Location : on B1120 Stowmarket to Yoxford Road.
Credit cards : not accepted.
Bitters : Adnams Best & Broadside.
Lagers : Carlsberg, Heineken Export.

Examples of bar meals (lunch & evening, 7 days - ALL DAY Sat & Sun in summer): *home-made steak & kidney pie; lasagne; veg. lasagne; fresh fish & chips; jacket potatoes; salads; sandwiches; daily specials eg liver & onion casserole, pork in cider sauce, Napoleon lamb, vegetable moussaka. Children's menu.*

Examples of restaurant meals (as above): *stir-fry beef; steaks; prawn provencal; lemon sole with herb & lemon butter; duck breast pan-fried with Dubonnet & redcurrant sauce; mushroom & nut stroganoff in filo pastry basket; daily specials eg beef stroganoff, Chinese loin of pork (noted). Sticky toffee pud; treacle tart; fruit crumbles; chocolate brandy mousse. Trad. Sun. roasts.*

New chef (since Feb. '95) Dean Slowley has made quite an impression, both on the scope and diversity of the menus and on the locality - a local newspaper gave rave reviews for his Chinese Pork. The pork comes from Adnams' award-winning farm, and other produce is also fresh and local as far as possible. Longstanding proprietors Alan and Eileen Doughty, themselves Suffolk people, extend a warm greeting to all-comers to their classic 15th-century country pub, full of character. Children are most welcome, and have colouring sets provided - the results are displayed on one wall. The garden has play equipment and barbecue. The 30-seater restaurant is a no-smoking area.

THE CROWN AT WESTLETON

Westleton, Saxmundham. Tel: (01728) 648777, Fax: (01728) 648239
INTERNET E-MAIL: reception@the crown.nemesis.co.uk

Location : village centre.
Credit cards : Access, Amex, Diners, Visa.
Accommodation : 17 doubles, 2 singles, private facilities in all. AA2* 73%.
Tourist Board 4 stars commended. Class 2 access for disabled.
Bitters : Adnams, 5 guests from 10 ind. regional brewers.
Lagers : Carlsberg, Red Stripe. Plus James White & Scrumpy Jack ciders.

Examples of bar meals (lunchtime & evening except Sat evening): *very fresh fish of the day (min. 5 dishes, cooked in various ways - speciality); steak & kidney pie with ale; stag & boar pie; pork casserole with cheese & herb dumplings; sirloin steak. Homemade treacle pudding; rum & raisin pudding. Children's menu.*

Examples from £17.50 table d'hote (evenings only): *grilled fillet of cod with light curry sauce, roast fillet of lamb carved on ratatouille. Chocolate cherry & cognac roulade. 'Jewels' menu (lunchtimes also, by request): breast of Suffolk guinea fowl with mango & stem ginger; beef Wellington; mille feuille of salmon & scallops on lemon cream sauce. Vegetarian menu. Trad. Sun. roasts. Bookings advised.*

This picturesque village has changed little, but Rosemary and Richard Price offer 'state-of-the-art' amenities: six Honeymoon rooms, some with four-posters or half-tester beds, all equipped with superb bathrooms complete with jacuzzi. Barbecues are held weekend lunchtimes (weather permitting) in the pleasant terraced garden, and a large conservatory is for the use of non-smokers. Inside has an open log fire which spits and crackles on a cold day - just right for a bowl of soup and a hunk of granary bread, now baked on the premises. World famous Minsmere Nature Reserve is just a few minutes' walk.

THE KING'S HEAD
High Street, Southwold. Tel: (01502) 724517

Location : main street, on right as approaching.
Credit cards : Access, Visa.
Accommodation : 3 dbls/twins (non-smoking). All en suite, TV, tea & coffee.
From £50 per room; single rate by negotiation.
Bitters : Adnams.
Lagers : Red Stripe, Carlsberg.

Examples from lunch menu (daily): *local fresh fish simply grilled; Adnams pork (noted); steak, kidney & Guinness pie; Orford honeyroast ham; chicken, ham & mushroom pie; curries; chilli; lasagne; homemade pate; jacket potatoes; ploughman's. Bakewell tart; fruit crumbles; sticky toffee pudding. Trad. Sun. roasts.*

Examples from evening menu (daily): *charcoal grilled steaks, fish & chicken; homemade pies; pasta & vegetarian dishes always.*

Southwold is famed for its easy-going pace of life, and dining at this 18th-century town-centre pub is intended to be a casual "come as you are" affair. Flexibility is the watchword: any reasonable request will be met, and as everything is prepared to order be ready to wait a little while in peak periods. Use the time to quaff some of the excellent Adnams ales or wines, which travel only a few yards from the brewery in the town (the pub has won the Adnams Cellar Award two years running), or study the pictures in the split-level timbered bar (formerly a grocery store). Sunday evenings are for Jazz and Blues buffs, when they are performed live. New bedrooms are very good value (as is the home-cooked food); take a brisk stroll to the beach before breakfast. Phil Goodacre earned a regular place in major guides during his nine years at other establishments, and looks set to do so here. Parking on street or nearby public car park.

ADNAMS & CO. PLC.
SOLE BAY BREWERY, SOUTHWOLD, SUFFOLK IP18 6JW
TEL: 01502 727200 FAX: 01502 727201

THE BELL INN
St Olaves, nr Gt Yarmouth. Tel: (01493) 488249

Location : on A143 by the bridge.
Credit cards : Mastercard, Visa, Diners, Eurocard, Switch.
Bitters : Woodfordes Wherry, Boddingtons, Whitbread, 3 guests.
Lagers : Stella Artois, Heineken, Heineken Export.

Examples of bar meals (lunch & evening, 7 days): *duck with apricot & orange sauce; steak & kidney pie; steak in ale pie; lasagne; chicken tikka; sweet & sour pork; bacon roly poly; giant mixed grill; fisherman's pie; vegetable stroganoff; vegetable kiev; Children's menu.*

Examples of restaurant meals (as above): *Bell manor pot (spec.); tournedos rossini; surf & turf; pork Normandy; honey-roast duck with cherry sauce; scampi in ale batter with crispy bacon; Dover sole with king prawns; plaice filled with prawns, with pineapple & hollandaise; broccoli & mushroom bake. Baileys Bash; jam roly poly; treacle sponge. Trad. Sun. roasts.*

NB: open all day from 8:30am (9am Sundays) during summer (no hot food between 2:30 and 5:30pm)

"Broadland's oldest pub" is certainly amongst its most picturesque, and benefits from a marvellous riverside location, but it is principally the fresh homecooked food, under the auspices of new management and chefs, that has reawakened local interest. Inside lives up to the promise of the exterior: very cosy, with exposed timbers and brickwork, open fires, thick carpeting and upholstery. A secret passage from the priory - an escape route for monks - is said to run underneath, and a spectral Grey Lady is thought to be behind mysterious happenings. Red letter days are observed with special menus and there are monthly themes during winter - ask to go on mailing list. Great venue for wedding receptions etc. Barbecues by the river. Children welcome.

THE FERRY INN

Ferry Road, Reedham. Tel: (01493) 700429, Fax: (01493) 700999

Location : by River Yare, on B1140.
Credit cards : Access, Visa, Mastercard, Switch, Delta, Diners.
Accommodation : adjacent 4-acre caravan & camp site, full facilities.
Bitters : Woodfordes, Adnams, Tetley, Kilkenny.
Lagers : Holsten Export, Tuborg Gold, Carlsberg.

Examples of bar meals (lunch & evening 7 days): *vol-au-vent (chicken in creamy asparagus sauce); poached egg florentine; flaked fillets of smoked trout with horseradish sauce; steak sandwich; curry; lasagne; prawn Newburg; halibut steak with lemon, chervil & chive butter; braised local pheasant; devilled lambs' kidneys; pork fillet stuffed with smoked ham, fresh sage; mozarella, on mustard sauce; charcoal grills; vegetarian choux pastry case; salads; sandwiches; daily specials incl. sweets. Children's menu. Trad. Sun. roasts £5.50 main course.*

The last working chain ferry in East Anglia has been operating since the 16th century, and remarkably is still the only crossing point in over 20 miles. The inn is therefore guaranteed fame of a kind, but the Archers, who run both it and the ferry, make it worth a call on its own merit. Apart from serving good home-made food in clean and pleasant surrounds (one of the two dining rooms - bookable for functions - is no-smoking), they are considerate hosts, offering to make up a bottle for the baby and providing changing facilities in the ladies washroom, for example. Older children are well accommodated in a large sun lounge with arcade machines overlooking the river. From the table and chairs on the bank one can watch the various craft ply the waters. There are moorings and a slipway for trailed boats, and next to the inn a landscaped four-acre caravan and camping site with full facilities (incl. electric hook-ups and free hot water), plus an interesting woodcraft shop. Petits Feathercraft/Theme Park is very near.

In what year did this ferryman's cottage become a pub?

THE FERRY INN

The Green, Stokesby. Tel: (01493) 751096

Location : riverside, near village green.
Credit cards : not accepted.
Bitters : Adnams, Tolly's, guest.
Lagers : Stella Artois, Heineken.

Examples of bar meals (lunch & evening, 7 days): *pork fillets in sweet & sour sauce; chilli; curry; Norfolk garden pies; steaks; lasagne; fresh Cromer crab; natural plaice in lemon butter sauce; trout; Ferryman's lunch; salads; vegetarian lasagne; 4 daily specials. Cheesecake; fruit pies; gateaux. Children's menu. Trad. Sun. roasts.*

Stokesby is one of Broadland's finest: picturesque, tranquil, unspoilt, all the better for being off the beaten track. The river is probably busier than the road in summer, and many of the boats pull in to this eye-catching 18th-century former cottage, right on the water's edge and rated by major national guides. Inside will not disappoint: wooden settles and beams, corner seats and brassware. The cottage origins are most evident in the the large two-tier family lounge, whose concession to the 20th century is a few electronic games in one corner by the entrance. But in kind weather children will want to sit out by the river or head for the play area on the village green. A board on the terrace describes how there was once a ferry across the river, and will provide the answer to the question above!

THE HORSE & GROOM

Main Road, Rollesby, nr Gt Yarmouth. Tel: (01493) 740624, Fax: (01493) 740022

Location : on A149.
Credit cards : Access, Visa, Mastercard, Switch, Amex, Delta.
Accommodation : 20 rooms (sleep 2 - 4). All en suite, free satellite TV, direct phone, radio alarm, tea & coffee. Some rooms suitable for disabled. £33.95 per room (large family rooms £41.95). EATB 3-Crown Commended. Grade 2 disabled facility.
Bitters : Flowers Original, Boddingtons, IPA.
Lagers : Stella Artois, Heineken.

Examples of bar meals (lunch & evening, 7 days): *fresh salmon with hollandaise sauce; home-made steak & kidney pie; fresh haddock mornay; beef curry; moules mariniere; grilled fresh plaice fillets; roast Norfolk turkey; fresh trout pan-fried in lemon butter. Home-made cheesecakes; treacle tart; blackberry & apple pie.*

Examples of restaurant meals (as above): *stilton & mushroom pot; coquille St Jacques; devilled whitebait; home-made pate; soup of the day. Fresh turbot in scallop sauce; halibut in bearnaise sauce; brill in shrimp sauce; steak Diane, steak roquefort; T-bone steaks; home-made pies. Trad. Sun. roasts £7.75 & £9.50 (2 & 3 courses).*

Anyone with a taste for good fresh seafood should circle Rollesby on the map. The amazing choice chalked up on blackboards here is an inventory of the North Sea - Lowestoft is only a few miles away and shellfish comes from North Norfolk. Chris and Ann Carter built an excellent reputation at their former pub, the Bell at Brisley, and have done so again since coming to the Horse & Groom in July '91. Of course there are alternatives to seafood (sweets are very popular), and pride is taken that all is home-cooked and fresh, and good value at an average of £5 for a bar meal. The bedrooms are also incredible value for such a high standard, and so well placed for business or touring. The lounge bar and restaurant are also very comfortably appointed. Well-behaved children welcome. Garden.

THE FISHERMAN'S RETURN

The Lane, Winterton-on-Sea. Tel: (01493) 393305/393631

Location : near village centre and fine sandy beach.
Credit cards : pending.
Accommodation : 3 doubles. £30 single, £45 dbl incl. Rooms are quaint with sloping
ceilings. Tea & coffee. facilities. 2 bathrooms, 2 sitting rooms with TV.
Bitters : Adnams, Bass, John Smiths, unusual guests.
Lagers : Holsten, Fosters, Kronenbourg. Plus James White & Scrumpy Jack cider.

Examples of bar meals (lunch & evening 7 days): *leek & mushroom soup with french bread; deep-fried camembert with port jelly; chicken & leek tagliatelle; carbonnade of beef with savoury wild rice; Caribbean pork; fresh salmon provencale; vegetable Madras; aubergine & red kidney bean casserole. Plum & apple crumble; lemon lush pie; strawberry-topped cheesecake; hot chocolate fudge cake.*

The windows were once permanently boarded up, as so many bodies were thrown through them when the fishing fleet returned! These days customers usually enter by the door, and find themselves in surprisingly roomy, converted 300-year-old fishermen's cottages. The maritime theme pervades the bars in the form of old photographs and seascapes. In winter the open fires broadcast their warm welcome - the winds off the sea are bracing at times. To the rear a spacious room for families overlooks a patio and garden with swings. There is also a large room for functions, seating 40 or 60 buffet-style. This strange and beautiful coast is a marvellous spot to recharge one's spirits, and for a more prolonged stay there are three charming bedrooms, old fashioned but comfortable. All is homecooked to a standard which routinely earns credit from Egon Ronay and other leading guides. Good choice of at least 20 malt whiskies, 13 wines and champagne. Dart board.

THE FUR & FEATHER INN

Woodbastwick, nr Norwich. Tel: (01603) 720003

Location : on main road through village.
Credit cards : not accepted.
Bitters : full Woodfordes range.
Lagers : Heineken, Stella Artois.

Examples of bar/restaurant meals (lunch & evening, 7 days): *chicken & mushroom croissant; pork spare ribs; home-made meatloaf; Woodforde's pie; Fur & Feather pie (local game in red wine gravy); Woodforde's Yorky; lemon sole goujons; seafood tagliatelle; ½lb burger topped with prawns; veggie burger; canneloni, spinach & ricotto; leek & stilton bake; steaks & grills; breast of magret duck in cranberry & orange compot. Chocolate & hazelnut cheesecake; spotted dick; treacle sponge; lemon meringue.*

NB: restaurant open Tues-Sat evenings, bar food every session.

This being the Brewery Tap, the full range of Woodforde's cask-conditioned ales (available in take-home casks), including more than one national 'champion', is dispensed to eager devotees. It has only a few yards to travel from the brewery next door. But this is no mere drinker's den: cleverly converted by John Marjoram, Jean Skelton and Woodfordes from 19th-century farm cottages in 1992, one of Norfolk's newer pubs quickly became one of its most popular, not just for the beer but for a surprisingly wide choice of traditional homecooked food served in pleasant surroundings. Live entertainment is planned for winter - ask for details. Take time to see the village itself, a throwback to an earlier age, with cottages and a church clustered around a green, and not a car in sight. Lovely Salhouse Broad is also an easy walk.

COLDHAM HALL TAVERN

Coldham Hall Carnser, Surlingham. Tel: (01508) 538591

Location : riverside, ¾mile from village (signposted).
Credit cards : Mastercard, Visa.
Bitters : Bateman's XB & XXXB, Shepherd Neame Spitfire,
Tetley, guest from wood.
Lagers : Carlsberg, Heineken, Stella Artois.

Examples of bar meals (lunch & evening, 7 days, except Boxing Day): *pork ribs in barbecue sauce; poached salmon in rosemary sauce; steaks; rack of lamb roasted in mulled wine, with apricot sauce; large Scottish scampi tails in light crispy coating; oak-smoked local trout; "desperate Dan" steak & kidney pie; hot Fenland ham in red-currant & cinnamon sauce; half roast Norfolk chicken with herbs & butter; many daily specials eg steak & kidney pudding, local game, liver & bacon casserole, sword-fish steak broquettes. Home-made strawberry pavlova; apple pie; spotted dick, gateaux. Traditional Sunday roasts.*

It is one of summer's simple joys to sit in the landscaped garden or its pagoda here on a sweep of the River Yare, pint in hand, idly watching the colourful sails gliding past - a wonderful venue for a wedding reception. Many boaters reserve moorings at this alluring and ancient tavern (once a hunting lodge to royalty), and they don't go away disappointed: beer is well kept, food is home-made and served in portions likely to cause the craft to lie a little deeper in the water. In the past it was a favourite amongst wherrymen, who also liked to 'pull oars' in the brothel in neighbouring cottages! A tranquil winter's day has charms of its own, not least an open fire in the double-breasted inglenook, an equally warm welcome from the staff, and the same fine view from the dining room. Red Letter days are observed and there's occasional live music, plus pool and darts. The famous Ted Ellis Nature Reserve is only yards away.

To what rather unusual intended pub
name did locals object?

THE MAD MOOSE ARMS

2 Warwick Street, Norwich. Tel: (01603) 627687

Location: turn into Dover Street by parade of shops on Unthank Road.
Credit cards: Mastercard, Visa, Switch, Delta, Amex, Diners.
Bitters: Old Speckled Hen, Courage Best & Directors, John Smith's,
John Smith's Smooth.
Lagers: Holsten Export, Fosters, Kronenbourg, Miller.

Examples of bar meals (11am to 2:30pm, 5:30 to 10:30pm Mon - Sat; 11am to 10pm Sundays): *hot & sour Thai soup; crispy bacon & banana; devilled chicken; smoked fish chowder; Panang beef balls & peanut sauce; bruschetta with roasted peppers, basil & tomato; spiced escalope of salmon with mango & black bean sauce; Peking crispy duck with pancakes & hoisin sauce; smoked haddock & salmon fishcake with piquant creme fraiche; Afghan rice pudding; Tahitian banana fritters; rich chocolate pot. Trad. Sun. roasts.*

The uproar which greeted the name originally intended (see 'Trivia' question) made national news, but the one finally chosen is appropriate enough to this stablemate of the celebrated Wildebeest Arms at Stoke Holy Cross (qv). The Mad Moose opened in November 1995 under the stewardship of Andrew Wilkins, and neighbours will need to get used to the opening 'stampede': a combination of refreshingly modern good food, fine ales and a markedly informal atmosphere is bringing in a healthy mix of customers. It's only two minutes' drive from the city centre (where there's another stablemate, Hector's House), and indeed has the feel of a London pub, with stripped oak floors, high ceilings and windows. Children welcome. Barbecues in garden.

THE WILDEBEEST ARMS

Norwich Road, Stoke Holy Cross. Tel: (01508) 492497

Location : village centre, 2 mins off the A140.
Credit cards : Mastercard, Visa, Switch, Delta, Diners, Amex.
Bitters : Adnams, Courage Directors & Best, John Smiths.
Lagers : Fosters, Holsten, Kronenbourg, Miller.

Examples of bar meals (lunch & evening, 7 days): *pigeon breast with turnip & apple chou-croute & blackcurrant sauce; tart of fresh mussels, shallots & spicy curried mussel sauce; roasted peppers on large crouton with fresh basil & parmesan; fillet of sea bass with crab & herb crust, fresh tagliatelle & leek sauce; rack of lamb with pesto, fresh ratatouille & red wine sauce; tart of goats' cheese & spicy aubergine on red pepper coulis. Deep-fried vanilla ice cream, coated in coconut with blackcurrant compote; warm crouton of apple & brie with prune sauce; chocolate ganache mille-feuille with chocolate puff pastry & warm cherry sauce; daily specials. Trad. Sun. roasts. 'Menu du Jour' (3 courses for £12). Plainer food for children on request.*

This exciting new pub opened in autumn 1994 and received rave reviews in the local press; it is surely only a matter of time for recognition in the national guides. People are travelling a long way to eat here, and a glance over the few examples listed above indicates why: original and adventurous, it could hardly be described as typical pub food, and you can watch its preparation in the open kitchen. The selective wine list is well priced and of good quality. A distinctive African theme is established (although not overstated) in the long, single bar by authentic musical instruments and wood carvings. Because of its popularity booking is always advisable. The Wildebeest is one of the trio which includes Hector's House and the new Mad Moose Arms (qv) in Norwich. Children welcome. Garden.

THE BIRD IN HAND
Church Road, Wreningham. Tel: (01508) 489438

Location : 8 miles South of Norwich on B1113.
Credit cards : Access, Visa, Amex.
Bitters : Adnams, Marstons Pedigree, Fullers London Pride, Bass, Caffreys,
       Boddingtons, weekly guest.
Lagers : Stella Artois, Heineken.

Examples of bar meals (12 to 2pm, 6:30 to 10pm; Sundays 5.30 to 9.30): *homemade pies (eg steak & kidney pie; venison cranberry & redcurrant, wild boar & calvados, chestnut brocolli & baby corn.); mushroom & brandy stroganoff; pork fillets with orange & port; lasagne; curry; whole-tail scampi; filled jacket potatoes; fresh-baked rolls; daily specials eg Dover sole, guinea fowl, honey & mint lamb cutlets, sea bass with a prawn hollandaise, pan fried chicken supreme with fresh chilli sauce.*

Examples from a la carte: *salmon cream cheese mousse; trio of sorbets; garlic, tomato baked mushrooms; quenelles of Ardennes pate & melba toast; venison-filled guinea fowl breast wrapped in bacon; poached Scottish salmon with crab & lobster cream; fillet steak marinated in Thai spices; French duck breast with kumquats; very special homemade desserts. 3-course Sunday roasts (booking advised).*

Carol Turner arrived here seven years ago armed with qualifications from the British Institute of Innkeeping and high expectations. They have been exceeded, necessitating a staff of 28, including three chefs. The continuing success of the business and quality of service have been recognised in National Industry Awards! There are appetising menus, but the beautiful interior, far surpassing the promise of the exterior, is also quite exceptional. The bar was once a stable, and that special farmhouse ambience is unmistakable; the Victorian restaurant is furnished most handsomely. Well behaved children welcome, and there's a large landscaped beer garden. Weddings and private parties a speciality. Conference facilities. Superb washrooms!

THE KING'S HEAD

Bawburgh, nr Norwich. Tel: (01603) 744977, Fax: (01603) 744990

Location : village centre.
Credit cards : Mastercard, Visa, Switch, Amex.
Bitters : Fuggles, Adnams, Marstons Pedigree, Boddington, Flowers IPA, 2 guests.
Lagers : Stella Artois, Heineken & Heineken Export.

Examples of bar/restaurant meals (lunch & evening, 7 days): *seafood crepe; home-made pies; roast honey & lime chicken; sausages & mash; lasagne; chilli; curry; steaks; fresh fish daily; mushroom & quorn casserole; veg. pie; duck-egg omelette; jacket potatoes; salads; sandwiches; many daily specials eg flaked crab crumble, large parrot fish in vine leaf & lemon grass with dill & ginger glaze, ragout of Norfolk hare, roast wild boar with sauce of port & woodland mushroom, ostrich, alligator, kangaroo! Chocolate delice; shortbread chantilly; bread & butter pudding. Children's menu. Trad. Sun. roasts.*

Much more than just a pub - The King's Head is a rarity, not just for the four squash courts and Crown Green bowls, but also for the highly creative and unusual food. Whether staunchly traditional, such as sausages and mash, or exotica like kangaroo or ostrich, all is fresh and prepared with pride by head chef Adrian and second chef Chris. The choice of beers and wines is also exceptional. The inn has stood by the river running through this quaint little village since 1602, and is full of character. No games machines assault the senses, neither do cigarettes in the no-smoking room. Lee Vasey plays live alternate Monday evenings, and there are numerous special themes and promotions. Landlady Pamela Wimmer is now joined in the business by son Anton. Function room for up to 80. Children welcome. Sheltered courtyard.

THE UGLY BUG INN

Colton, nr Norwich. Tel: (01603) 880794

Location : in village
Credit cards : Mastercard, Visa,
       Switch, Delta, Eurocard.
Accommodation : 1 single (£27),
       1 twin (en suite),
       1 family with bathroom
       (both £45). Tea & Coffee.
Bitters : Ugly Bug, Greene King, 2 guests.
Lagers : Carlsberg, Kronenbourg.

Examples of bar meals (lunch & evening, 7 days): *pie of the day; steak of the day; veg. curry; pan-fried sardines in garlic butter; king scallops sauted with pesto; mushrooms in warm croissant; home-made savoury tomato doughnuts with mozarella; bison sausages; squid ink spaghetti; h/m black pudding.*

Examples of restaurant meals (as above): *rabbit casserole; fresh salmon with white truffle sauce; goose breast roasted with plum sauce; conger eel dipped in seeds & baked; roast poussin with h/m chestnut & granary crumb stuffing; liver & bacon; sea bass in prawn sauce with ecrivisse & sea veg. garnish; shark steaks. Apple & marmalade crumble; lemon & mascarpone cheesecake; spotted dick; quality Swiss ice creams.*

The odd name is not at all apt, for this striking conversion stands in over three acres of the most beautifully landscaped gardens (with barbecue), complete with carp stream and floodlit bridge. Inside, you will find it warm and congenial, replete with timbers, exposed brickwork and cottagey furniture. The restaurant seats 58 and there's also a conservatory for private parties, small wedding receptions etc. Since opening in 1991 Peter and Sheila Crowland have established a reputation for good, homecooked food, including numerous ingenious and exotic dishes from their new chef, plus excellent ales, recognised by CAMRA and leading good beer guides. Children are welcome and the Dinosaur Park is nearby. Monthly quiz nights.

*What was discovered under the
floorboards during renovations?*

THE OLD RAM

Tivetshall St Mary. Tel: (01379) 676794, Fax: (01379) 608399

Location: on A140 south of Norwich.
Credit cards: Access, Visa, Switch.
Accommodation: 5 rooms (inc. 2 suites), all en suite. Satellite TV, trouser press, hair dryer,
direct phone, tea & coffee.
Bitters: Adnams, Woodfordes, Ruddles County, Boddingtons.
Lagers: Fosters, Holstein, LA.

Examples of bar meals (7:30am - 10pm every day): *Ram grill (spec.); rack of pork ribs; barbecue chicken; fruits de mer; trout with toasted almonds; steak & kidney pie; lasagne; moussaka; chilli; chicken curry; steaks; salads; filled rolls; aubergine & mushroom bake; extensive choice of chef's specials incl. wide variety of fresh fish. Large selection of gateaux eg raspberry torte; white chocolate cheesecake; chocolate ganache; fromaggio.*

No matter at what time, the car park of this 17th-century coaching inn seems always to be quite full - even at four in the afternoon! It is without doubt one of the most popular hostelries in the entire region, with a name that goes well beyond. The reasons are not hard to discern: as well as being open all day from 7:30am, the menu is enormous, and comprised of good, wholesome favourites, served in belt-loosening portions and in an amiable, lively atmosphere. Not surprisingly, then, it features in just about every major national guide, a credit to John Trafford, who with wife Julie has built this enviable success over the past eight years. Special occasions are honoured - roses for ladies on Valentine's Night, Beaujolais, Mothering Sunday, and others. Children welcome. Large garden. No expense has been spared to make the accommodation quite superb.

*In what year were the last courts
held in the Old Court Restaurant?*

THE CROWN HOTEL & RESTAURANT
Crown Road, Mundford. Tel: (01842) 878233

Location : village centre, just off A1065.
Credit cards : Access, Visa, Diners, Amex.
Accommodation : 2 singles (£29.50), 5 doubles (£45). New Coach House with beautifully
appointed rooms & Reception Room opened in Oct '95.
Bitters : Woodfordes Wherry & Nelson's Revenge, Websters,
local-brewed Iceni beers, Sam Smiths, Directors.
Lagers : Fosters, Carlsberg, Holsten Export, Kronenbourg.

Examples of bar meals (lunch & evening, 7 days): *chicken breast with bacon & stilton cream; leek & gruyere strudel served on fresh tomato sauce; homemade lamb kebabs; fresh fish (speciality) with classic & unexpected sauces; many daily blackboard specials.*

Examples of restaurant meals (as above): *scallop & mange tout salad; field mushrooms & hot garlic cottage prawns. Noisettes of lamb with fresh mint & balsamic vinegar; sea bass fillet with smoked marlin. Trad. Sun. roasts. Booking always advised.*

NB: Open all day; food served 12 to 3pm, 7 to 10pm (last orders).

The Crown has gained recognition for its food in the principal national guides, based on the daily specials and a la carte menus, anything from home-made soups to a classic medley of Ickburgh duck, served in typical Norfolk portions, with prices starting at under £2. Many regulars have also been gained through 'Norfolk Pub Walks' (this being good walking country). In its time (from 1652) The Crown has also been a hunting lodge and doctor's surgery, and, perhaps uniquely in Norfolk, is built on the side of a small hill, so that one may walk in to the ground floor bar and exit from the first floor restaurant into the garden - glorious in summer. All in all, a lovely inn to stop off for good food, lively company and comfortable accommodation.

THE CHEQUERS

Griston Road, Thompson, nr Thetford. Tel. (01953) 483360

Location: one mile off A1075.
Credit cards: Access, Visa, Diners, Mastercard, Eurocard.
Bitters: Adnams, Bass, Tetleys, Worthington, Caffreys, 2 guests.
Lagers: Carlsberg, Tennents.

Examples of bar meals (lunch & evening, 7 days): *home-made mackerel & tomato paté; local cockles; steaks; steak & kidney pie; lasagne; Cromer crab topped with cheese; trout almondine; mammoth mixed grill; barbecue spare ribs; mushroom & nut fettucini; salads; pizza; jacket potatoes; ploughman's; sandwiches; many daily specials eg beef & oyster pie, local game pie, fresh fish dishes. Fruit pies; cheesecake; chocolate fudge cake. Trad. Sun. roasts.*

One of the region's most picturesque pubs is also one of the best known and most frequented. Parts of it date from the 14th century or earlier, and the tiled flooring, exposed brickwork and timber beams are all original and incredibly well preserved. The three bars each have their own character, and significantly different ceiling heights - a headache for those who forget! One may eat in any of them, and there's a snug for children. But many choose to enjoy the rural peace in the garden (with play area), and the scene when all the hanging baskets are in flower is a joy to behold. Run by Bob and Wendy Rourke since 1988 and lauded by national guides, The Chequers also enjoys a very good reputation for food, with many blackboard specials supplementing an already good-sized menu. Not one to be missed, even though it is a little out of the way.

THE GREAT DANE'S HEAD

The Green, Beachamwell, nr Swaffham. Tel: (01366) 328443

Location : on village green, opp. church.
Credit cards : not acepted.
Bitters : Greene King Abbot, IPA, guest.
Lagers : Harp, Kronenbourg.

Examples of bar/restaurant meals (lunch & evening, 7 days): *homemade steak & kidney pie; game pie; turkey & stilton pie; noisettes of lamb; steaks; traditional paella; Cajun chicken; chicken Wellington; spicy beef; seafood parcel; seafood tagliatelle; sweet & sour prawns; wing of skate; trout; game in season.*

The three pub signs will bewilder the unwary: one shows the head of a large dog; another that of a Viking; a third tells us this is 'The Hole in the Wall'. It was in fact once known as The Cooper's Arms, but as there was no bar beer was served through a hole in the wall. Well, this is Norfolk. And Beachamwell is one of the county's many secrets, for it's a lovely, unspoilt village in the middle of nowhere, distinguished by the only thatched church with a round tower in Norfolk - it's very, very old. The pub commands a perfect view of it over the classic village green. Built around 1820 (although the cellar is older), it has recently been refurbished by Frank and Jenny White, who have made it very popular for good, homecooked food in generous portions at reasonable prices. Staple favourites rub shoulders with the exotic, augmented by theme nights such as Thai. One can sit in the garden in summer. Pool table. B & B in village.

THE HARE ARMS

Stow Bardolph, nr Downham Market. Tel: (01366) 382229, Fax: (01366) 385522

Location : off A10 between King's Lynn (9 miles) and Downham Market (2 miles).
Credit cards : Mastercard, Visa, Switch, Delta.
Bitters : Greene King.
Lagers : Kronenbourg, Harp.

Examples of bar meals (lunch & evening daily): *homemade chilli; curry; lasagne; steaks; salads; ploughman's; sandwiches; daily specials eg sea bream with red pepper sauce, salmon fillet with dill hollandaise, beef Guinness & oyster pie, vegetarian selection. Children's menu. Bar food served in restaurant Sun. lunchtimes.*

Examples of restaurant meals (a la carte Mon - Sat evenings, bookings advised): *tasty stilton paté with walnuts & celery; tiger prawns in spicy tomato sauce, flavoured with garlic & served on bed of rice; salmon fillet cooked in paper parcel with chopped root ginger, spring onions, garlic & julienne of vegetables; prime fillet steak stuffed with chopped oysters, mushrooms, bacon & blue cheese, coated on oyster-flavour sauce; succulent duck breast marinated in garlic, balsamic vinegar & rosemary, cooked pink & served sliced in red wine sauce. Also table d'hote (£16.75) Mon-Thurs. Trad. Sun. roast.*

Pleasantly situated in a small village, this popular ivy-clad inn has been recommended by Egon Ronay 14 years running for the delicious wholesome fare, and was also named Regional Pub of the Year 1993 in the Eastern Daily Press. Fresh local produce is used whenever possible - crab and lobster in summer, pheasant, pigeon and game in winter. The high-standard restaurant, a beautifully proportioned room, offers a menu of traditional and international dishes changed frequently. The 'Old Coach House' is available for a variety of functions, from private dinner or office parties to weddings (and family use on Sundays). Families are also welcome in the roomy conservatory or attractive garden.

119

THE ROSE & CROWN
Nethergate Street, Harpley, nr Fakenham. Tel: (01485) 520577

Location : off A148 King's Lynn to Fakenham road (opp. Houghton turn-off).
Credit cards : not accepted.
Bitters : Bass, Tetley.
Lagers : Stella Artois, Castlemaine.

Examples of bar meals (lunch & evening, 7 days): *mushrooms in creamy garlic sauce on French bread; deep-fried broccoli with blue cheese dip; seafood feast; salmon & broccoli pie; chicken korma; steak, Guinness & mushroom pie; half roast duck in orange sauce; steaks; chilli; lasagne; plaice; scampi; crunchy-topped bean casserole; pizzas; jacket potatoes; ploughman's. Homemade apple flan; syrup tart; warm chocolate fudge cake; poached pears in red wine. Children's menu. Trad. Sun. roasts (booking advised).*

This attractive 17th-century pub is waiting to be discovered just a few seconds' drive off the busy A148, in one of the loveliest parts of the region, near to Peddars Way and Sandringham. Under the ownership of Michael and Liz Kentfield since spring '89, it is popular with locals and visitors alike - families are especially welcome. The sizable menu is a blend of traditional favourites with a little overseas influence to add zest. The home cooking may be enjoyed in bar or separate dining room. Pool, darts dominoes and crib are the indoor amusements, outside there's an enclosed garden with play area and occasional barbecues. Michael and Liz also run a successful outside catering service, weddings etc.

THE CROWN

Colkirk, nr Fakenham. Tel: (01328) 862172

Location: village centre.
Credit cards: Access, Visa, Mastercard.
Bitters: Greene King IPA & Abbot, Rayments Special.
Lagers: Harp, Kronenbourg.

Examples of bar meals (lunch & evening, 7 days): *gratin of mushrooms & prawns; duck liver & armagnac paté; hot Thai chicken; home-made soups; fresh fish of the day; prime Scotch steaks; braised lambs' kidneys; casseroles; curries; vegetarian selection. Homemade hot puddings; gateaux; cheesecake; extensive cheeseboard.*

Folk in these parts seem to be unanimous in praise of their local, and it is hard to find fault with such an honest example of the English country pub at its best. The food is fresh and home cooked, the bar and dining room comfortable and pleasant, and the atmosphere congenial. Traditional games like skittles, shove ha'penny, darts and dominoes provide amusement. In winter, warm the extremities with a good hot meal by an open fire; in summer do the same in the sun on the patio or in the beer garden (formerly a bowling green), perhaps with a bottle of wine from an extensive, personally selected list, all available by the glass - The Crown is noted as one of the top five wine pubs in the country. Pat and Rosemary Whitmore are your amicable hosts, well established here over many years.

THE BOAR INN
Gt Ryburgh, nr Fakenham. Tel: (01328) 829212

Location : end of village, opp. 13th-century church.
Credit cards : Access, Visa, Connect.
Accommodation : 1 single, 1 double, 2 twins.
Bitters : Wensum (own brand), Adnams, Greene King, Burtons, Tetley, Kilkenny.
Lagers : Carlsberg, Lowenbrau.

Examples of bar/restaurant meals (lunch & evening, 7 days): *mushroom royale (cooked with stilton & garlic); lasagne; steak & kidney pie; Madras beef curry; salads; steaks; chicken cordon bleu; barbecue lamb cutlets; salmon steak in mushroom & cream sauce; rahmschnitzel; chicken tikka; steaks; prawn creole; daily specials. Meringue glace; fruit crumble; Italian ices.*

All is cooked to order here, so allow a little extra time to be served at peak periods. A short stroll to the clear River Wensum, which meanders through a meadow just yards to the rear of the shaded, rose-scented garden (the patio is a sun trap) would fill the time nicely. Or take the opportunity to look around this ancient inn; the cosy beamed bar is warmed by an open fire in winter, and the dining room is also very attractive and spacious. Just across the road is an excellent example of the country church for which Norfolk is famed. All this plus a comprehensive, international menu has regularly secured an entry in more than one national guide. In the heart of the county, The Boar makes for a marvellous rural retreat, ideal for an extended visit and perhaps for a hair-do at the salon on the premises!

THE CHEQUERS INN

Front Street, Binham, nr Fakenham. Tel: (01328) 830297

Location : village centre, on B1388 between Wells and Walsingham.
Credit cards : not accepted.
Accommodation : Single £22, dbl £36, family £40 per room incl. TV's, tea & coffee.
Bathroom adjacent.
Bitters : Adnams Best, Woodfordes Wherry, Bass, Highgate Park, Toby, guests.
Lagers : Carling, Tennents Extra.

Examples of bar meals (lunch & evening, 7 days): *fresh homemade soups; trad. English breakfast; steak & kidney pie; homecooked meats; cod/plaice; whole tail scampi; vegetarian dishes; sandwiches; salads; daily specials eg liver & bacon casserole, pork fillet with apricot, beef & vegetables cooked in ale. Evening specials include fresh local fish and steaks. Trad. Sun. roasts £5.50 (2 courses), 12 - 2pm.*

NB Open all day Thurs - Sat., usual Sunday hours.

One of Norfolk's finest villages, famed for its priory, Binham is also blessed with one of the county's foremost freehouses, standing in one acre. Unusual in that the freehold belongs to the village itself, the 17th-century Chequers has been ably run since January 1991 by Brian Pennington and Barbara Garratt, both very experienced. They share the cooking, using only the freshest and best of produce. Prices are exceptional: a huge T-bone with all the trimmings is just £9.95, for example. Accommodation is also good value. The building itself oozes character; of special interest is an engraving of the Battle of Portsmouth, during which the Mary Rose sunk. Well-behaved children welcome. Indoor games. Large garden. Occasional music nights (especially in winter). Handy for all the attractions of this lovely area.

THE KINGS ARMS

Westgate Street, Blakeney. Tel. (01263) 740341

Location : near quayside, west end of village.

Credit cards : Access, Visa.

Accommodation : self-contained holiday flatlets, £50 in summer, £30 winter, incl. breakfast.

Bitters : Norwich, Webster, Ruddles, Marston's Pedigree, guests.

Lagers : Fosters, Carlsberg.

Examples of bar meals (lunch & evening, 7 days; all day weekends & children's holidays): *home-made pies; seafood pasta; local crabs; mussels; prawns; salads; vegetarian dishes; steaks; fresh cod; local trout; salmon; gammon steaks; scampi; daily specials.*

NB All-day opening, every day.

Blakeney would be many people's choice for East Anglia's most picturesque village. Its flint cottages, alleys and courtyards are a delight on the eye, and the views from the quayside over the marshes provide a lovely backdrop. Just off the quayside, The King's Arms was once three narrow fishermen's cottages, but is now one of the most popular pubs in the area, recommended by national guides. Howard and Marjorie Davies left the world of the Black and White Minstrels and My Fair Lady 23 years ago and took over from the previous landlord who'd reigned for 45 years! They welcome children (who have their own room, and swings in the large garden) and even dogs if the bar is not full (which in summer it usually is). Smokers themselves may appreciate the facility of a no-smoking room to enjoy the good food. See if you can spot the 1953 flood tide mark on an inside wall.

THE WHITE HORSE HOTEL & FREEHOUSE
4 High Street, Blakeney. Tel: (01263) 740574

Location : village centre.
Credit card s: Access, Visa, Amex.
Accommodation : 2 singles, 4 doubles, 1 twin, 2 family, all en suite bathrooms, TV's, tea & coffee. From £30 pp incl. Special rates for children and winter breaks.
Bitters : Adnams, Boddingtons, Flowers.
Lagers : Stella Artois, Heineken.

Examples of bar meals (lunch & evening, 7 days): *deep fried herring roes on toast; local whitebait; mussels; fisherman's pie; sirloin steak; local crabs; vegetarian dishes; daily specials eg homemade steak & kidney pudding, tagliatelle with smoked salmon & broccoli sauce, mushroom & stilton pancakes. Spotted dick; treacle tart; bread & butter pudding.*

Examples of restaurant meals (evenings Tues - Sat; booking advised weekends): *chargrilled breast of pigeon with braised turnip & black pudding; poached garden pears with stilton & walnut mousse; grilled fillets of red mullet with spring onion & basil sauce; ballantine of chicken with crab sauce; roast fillet of lamb with sesame & herb crust on red wine sauce. Iced terrine of nougatine with raspberry sauce; grilled pear with hot chocolate sauce & honey & ginger ice cream.*

What a place for a weekend break - the views over the quay from some of the warm, very well appointed bedrooms are superb. The intimate little restaurant (converted from stables), overlooking the attractive walled courtyard, has acquired a sterling reputation for good food, accompanied by an excellent wine list. Chef Ray Maddox is formerly of the famous Langan's, and he relies heavily on fresh and mostly local produce, especially seafood. But if your fancy is simply a good pint and maybe a hearty bar meal, this freehouse is also eminently suitable. Residents car park in front of hotel. No dogs.

*When did the pub re-open after
26 years as a private house?*

THE STIFFKEY RED LION

44 Wells Road, Stiffkey, nr Wells. Tel: (01328) 830552, Fax: (01328) 855983

Location : on A149 coast road, 1 mile from marshes & coastal path.
Credit cards : Visa.
Bitters : Woodfordes (from the barrel), Greene King, guests.
Lagers : two rotating.

Examples of bar meals (lunch & evening, 7 days): *pan-fried liver & bacon with bubble & squeak; steak & kidney pie; roast chicken in tarragon sauce; local crab & mussels; vegetarian dishes; fresh baguettes with various fillings. Sponge puddings; treacle tart; spotted dick; summer pudding; strawberries & cream; local ice cream. Trad. Sun. roast.*

Stiffkey achieved notoriety through its erstwhile vicar, who wanted to save loose women and ended in the jaws of a lion. Being 16th-century, this Red Lion was there long before him, and would seem to have a piano-playing ghost who is given to moving barstools about! It's now the only pub left in one of Norfolk's most picturesque flint villages, but fortunately is one well worth stopping off for. With four open fires, stripped wood and tiled floors, old wooden settles and traditional pub games, the bar is simple and authentic. To the rear are a smart conservatory and dining room. Functions up to 40 are catered for, and outside bars and wedding receptions are gladly arranged. The new manager (since late '94) is keen on hospitality, and does welcome children. Service is as speedy as possible given that all is fresh and cooked to order (local produce favoured). Terrace overlooks lovely river valley. Large car park.

THE THREE HORSESHOES
Warham, nr Wells-next-Sea. Tel: (01328) 710547

Location : village centre.
Credit cards : under review.
Accommodation : 1 single, 2 doubles (1 en suite), + 2 s/c cottages in N.Creake.
Bitters : Woodfordes, Greene King, guests.
Lagers : Carlsberg.

Examples of bar/dining room meals (lunch & evening, 7 days): *smokie hotpot; game terrine; potted cheese & port; potted smoked fish; cheesy mushroom bake; haddock fillet in cheese sauce; fisherman's pie; rabbit pie; steak & beer pie; cheesy vegetable pie. Spotted dick, steamed syrup sponge, Nelson cake.*

This genuinely unspoilt 18th-century cottage pub will evoke memories of a less frantic age. It's totally 'un-modern', to the extent of a 1940's fruit machine in one corner. Bare floors, open fires, old furniture and gas lighting complete the agreeable illusion. What was the children's room is now a lounge, but families are still welcome, and the garden borders a stream and the village green. More space was needed in response to growing demand for fresh seafood at reasonable prices, the house speciality, and the menu includes many meat and vegetarian alternatives. Also good value is the accommodation, in a picturebook cottage with roses round the door and working water pump in the garden - an idyllic rural retreat in a timeless flint village.

127

THE LIFEBOAT INN
Ship Lane, Thornham, nr Hunstanton. Tel: (01485) 512236, Fax: (01485) 512323

Location: on a loop off A149 (signposted), overlooking harbour to sea.
Credit cards: Mastercard, Visa, Switch, Eurocard, Delta.
Accommodation: 13 dbls/twins. All en suite, TV, phone, hair-dryer, tea & coffee.
EATB 3 Crowns. From £30pp in winter, £32.50 in summer.
Special midweek & weekend breaks. Most rooms have panoramic views.
Bitters: Adnams, Woodfordes Wherry, Greene King, guests, own brew planned.
Lagers: Harp, Kronenbourg. Plus Scrumpy cider.

Examples of bar meals (lunch & evening, 7 days): *Thornham stuffed mushrooms; local oysters; Norfolk game pie; fish pie; fish & chips; steak; open sandwiches; ploughman's; daily specials eg jugged hare, wild boar, grilled goats' cheese with black olives, poached skate wing. Bread & butter pudding; apple crumble; chocolate delice.*

Examples of restaurant meals (as above): *Brancaster mussels (noted); prime fillet of local beef in madeira sauce with potato & fennel rosti; pan-fried duck breast on bed of glazed orange kumquats. Chocolate mousse cake with chantilly cream; sticky toffee pudding with butterscotch sauce; spotted dick. Trad. Sun. roasts. Afternoon teas.*

Little changed since the 15th century (the Smugglers' Bar is still lit by hanging oil lamps), this former smugglers' alehouse is widely acknowledged as one of the very best on this unique and lovely coast. Proprietors since June '95, Charles and Angie Coker do have plans for improvements - a children's bar, six more bedrooms and their own brewery! - but they are more than keen to safeguard the very special character of the place. This respect for tradition extends to the kitchen, where "catch of the day" local game and seafood is the house speciality. You may not need a lunch after one of their breakfasts! Guitarist often performs Friday evenings. Children's play area in garden.

THE GIN TRAP INN

High Street, Ringstead, nr Hunstanton. Tel: (01485) 525264

Location: village Centre.
Credit cards: not accepted.
Bitters: Greene King, Charrington, Worthington, Adnams, Toby,
Gin Trap Own, Woodfordes, guests.
Lagers: Carling, Tennents, Tennents L.A.

Examples of bar meals (lunch & evening, 7 days): *home-made lasagne; steak & kidney pie; steaks; freshly cut ham; scampi; plaice; vegetable sausages; vegetable tikka nuggets; nut cutlets.; daily specials eg h/m mushroom & sherry soup, fresh fish & chips, minced beef & veg. pie. Home-made bread & butter pudding; treacle pud; fruit crumbles; chocolate brandy crunch cake; sponge puds. Lunchtimes only: jacket potatoes; ploughman's; sandwiches. Children's menu. Trad. Sun. roasts £5.75.*

"25lb dragon steaks stuffed with hobbitt are available on 30th February, price £400.00" After a few pints of Gin Trap bitter you may feel tempted to tackle this most unlikely entry on the menu, but portions of more conventional fare are in truth generous, though prices somewhat more modest. Since acquiring this 17th-century coaching inn in 1987, Margaret and Brian Harmes have made this one of the area's most popular pubs, a favourite watering hole of ramblers, who are politely requested to remove muddy boots before walking on the monogrammed carpet! Countless gin traps have been cleverly adapted as light fittings, and rural implements of all kinds cover the ceiling. There are two car parks, one of which has stocks where miscreants were once pelted. Why not combine your visit with a look at the adjacent country and sporting art gallery? Walled beer garden. Occasional visits from Morris dancers, and regular entertainment at the piano.

THE FARMERS ARMS INN & RESTAURANT AT KNIGHTS HILL HOTEL

Knights Hill Village, South Wootton, King's Lynn. Tel: (01553) 675566

Location : on roundabout at intersection of A149 and A148.
Credit cards : Access, Visa, Diners, Amex.
Accommodation : 5 singles, 35 doubles, 12 twins, all en suite & with full facilities (some non-smoking). £70-£90 single, £80-£100 double. Weekend Breaks £57 pp per night (B & B plus £16.50 meal allowance).
Bitters : Adnams, Bass, Sam Smiths, Stones, Ruddles, guests.
Lagers : Carling, Tennents Extra, Tennents LA.

Examples of bar/restaurant meals (ALL DAY, EVERY DAY): *prawn & tomato basket; Farmer's Boots (deep-fried jacket potato skins with various fillings); salmon & broccoli crepe; seafood tagliatelle; steak & kidney pudding; gamekeeper's pie; lamb cobbler; chargrilled steaks, ribs & burgers; steak hogie; kebabs; cobs; salads; brown rice & hazelnut loaf; blackboard specials. "Basket of Sin"; rocky chocky choux; lemon lush pie; death by chocolate; luxury ice creams. Children's menu. Trad. Sun. lunch & full a la carte in hotel.*

Part of a unique 11-acre complex, The Farmers Arms was converted in 1986 from 17th-century working farm buildings, its rustic origins being quite unmistakable: flint walls, cobblestone floors, lots of 'snugs' (ideal for children), and a super function room in the old hayloft. The food is good and wholesome, very fair value, and bar snacks are available all day. Country music lovers should go along Wednesday nights. Petanque is played in the garden, and occasional barbecues held. Children's parties and wedding receptions are a speciality, and with a very smart hotel, health and leisure club and restaurant on the same site, every conceivable requirement is catered for.

TIDNAM'S TIPPLE AT THE ROSE & CROWN

Market Place, Wisbech. Tel: (01945) 589800, Fax: (01945) 474610

Location : on Market Square, town centre.
Credit cards : Access, Visa, Mastercard, Diners, Amex.
Accommodation : 3 sngls, 17 dbls/twins. All en suite, TV, direct phone, tea & coffee. Standard sngl £35, dbl £42.50; Executive sngl £47.50, dbl £52.50 per room. Eng. bkfst £5.50, Cont. £3.75. Special breaks from £80pp, 2 nights dinner, b & b.
Bitters : Greene King, Adnams, Ruddles, Bass, guest.
Lagers : Tennents, Tennents Extra, Carling.

Examples of bar meals (lunch & evening, 7 days): *Coach-house terrine with real ale; Fenland mushrooms (in garlic with cheddar); ploughman's pie; Lincolnshire sausage in onion gravy; tuna & pasta bake; steaks & grills; Indonesian chicken curry; sandwiches; daily specials eg steak & kidney pie, lasagne, lamb samosas. Chocolate shell filled with cherries in kirsch; spotted dick; Old English trifle.*

Examples of restaurant meals (as above): *banana Santa Lucia; melon & prawns Indienne; avocado Nicola. Grilled Dover sole; pork Dijonnaise; breast of duck in ginger & almond sauce; leek, potato & cheese bake. Death by chocolate; lemon lush; apple pie. Trad. Sun. roasts with alternatives £9.95 (3 courses).*

Prime amongst Wisbech's many handsome buildings is this 15th-century coaching inn, once again at the hub of the town's social and commercial life since change of ownership three years ago. Up to 150 people can be accommodated in the function room, and bedroom rates are very reasonable indeed. Adjacent in what were the stables, Tidnam's Tipple has become a popular refuge for those seeking straightforward and very tasty food (the choice is enormous) in an unhurried atmosphere. The adjacent courtyard is a quiet, sheltered spot in summer. The hotel has its own car park.

How many stables are left that were ran by the dogs?

THE RAMBLEWOOD INN AT ORTON HALL

Orton Longueville, Peterborough. Tel: (01733) 391111, Fax: (01733) 231912

Location : off A605 Oundle Road, 2 miles from city centre.
Credit cards : Mastercard, Visa, Switch, Delta, Diners, Amex.
Accommodation : 10 sngls (from £57.50), 29 dbls/twins (from £90), 2 family,
8 staterooms (some with 4-posters, from £100).
All en suite, TV, phone, dryer, tea & coffee.
Bitters : Caffreys, Bass, Fullers London Pride, Worthington,
3 ever-changing guests.
Lagers : Carling Black Label & Premier, Tennents Extra.

Examples of bar/dining room meals (lunch & evening, 7 days): *buffalo fries & dips; barbecue spare ribs; tuna & tomato bake; salmon & dill pasta; baked swordfish provencale; fisherman's pie; steak, mushroom & Guinness pudding; lamb balti with naan bread; chicken & leek pie; game cobbler; kleftico; steaks & grills; baguettes. H/m treacle & nut tart; chocolate fudge cake; Irish cream bash. Trad. Sun. roasts.*

Alternative dining available in main hotel in renowned Huntly Restaurant.

An imposing edifice standing in 22 acres of parkland, Orton Hall traces its origins back to 1086, and naturally has its crop of ghost stories. Close to Nene Park and several golf courses, and only minutes from the city, it is now well placed as a quality hotel and conference centre to suit the private or business person. But those seeking a good traditional pub have only a short walk across the courtyard to these former stables, superbly well converted, with exposed brickwork, high rafters, old saddles and rural implements all generating the right atmosphere. A split-level conservatory extension makes an airily agreeable dining room. The sizable and moderately priced menu is matched by a very good choice of ales. Occasional live music and theme evenings. Functions in the old hayloft. Children welcome.

YE OLDE WHITE HART

Main Street, Ufford, nr Stamford. Tel: (01780) 740250

Location : main road, village centre.
Credit cards : not accepted.
Accommodation : B & B in village may be arranged through pub.
Bitters : Theakston's Best & Old Peculier, Wadworth 6X, Home Bitter, 3 guests.
Lagers : Coors, Fosters.

Examples of bar meals (lunch & evening except Sun. evening & all day Mon.): *home -made beef & Guinness pie; baked avocado with stilton pate; home-made soups; chicken & leek pie; fresh plaice in lemon & caper butter; mushroom & asparagus hotpot; speciality Indian dishes; large baguettes with speciality sausages eg pork & stilton, Rutland garlic. Home-made sherry trifle; ginger sponge with lemon sauce; hot chocolate fudge cake. Trad. Sun. roasts.*

In the world of folk music Ye Olde White Hart figures prominently. Every Sunday evening and on the third Tuesday of each month top names from all over the world perform here; Iain Matthews, John Otway, members of Fairport Convention, Show of Hands, Albion Band and others love the matchlessly close and friendly atmosphere of this rustic 17th-century farmhouse - customers have travelled from as far as Amsterdam to join in. Folk is a great love of landlord Andy Tomblin (who, with wife Maggie, took over in June '95), but he is also a stickler for fresh home-made food, using quality local produce, and at very modest prices. Children are welcome; they will love the cuddly bunnies etc in the large, very pleasant garden, which commands a fine panorama over this lovely stone village. Functions up to 35 in dining room. Stamford, Burghley House and Nene Valley Railway all a few minutes' drive.

THE ADMIRAL WELLS

Station Road, Holme, nr Peterborough. Tel: (01487) 830730, Fax: (01487) 831159

Location: 2 miles off A1 at intersection of B660 with mainline railway.
Credit cards: Mastercard, Visa, Amex, Switch, JCB.
Bitters: Oakham JHB, Bass, Shepherd & Neame Spitfire, Hancocks HB, guests - all rotated (min. 7 real ales).
Lagers: Carling, Budvar.

Examples from lunch menu (daily): *home-made soup; cup mushrooms grilled with stilton & crusty bread; steak & kidney pie; seafood platter; cajun chicken; crispy cod; balti dishes; sandwiches. Apple strudel; treacle pud; peaches & cream pie. Traditional Sun. roasts. Examples from evening menu (not Sunday evenings, but also available weekend lunchtimes): smoked eel; artichoke pots with crusty bread; tuna & pasta bake; leek & stilton bake; salmon supreme in filo pastry with cheese & herb sauce; peppered fillet of pork with cream sauce; steaks.*

This is the lowest pub in Britain (actually below sea level), but in every other sense it is elevated well above the norm. Built in the mid-19th century, it is beautifully proportioned and elegant: high celings, doors and windows; stripped wood floors; brick fireplaces - hard to believe it was derelict until Christmas '94, which is when Stephen Kershaw (formerly a brewer) and Ian Miller (a lifelong publican) opened for business after a complete renovation. A new conservatory dining room (booking essential at weekends) overlooks a pleasant garden, field and orchard. To the rear are four floodlit petanque courts - darts and dominoes are the indoor pastimes. The menu is diverse and interesting enough, but special dishes can be prepared by arrangement, and barbecues are held in season. So why tolerate a plastic eaterie when all this is just a few minutes off the A1?

THE CROSS KEYS

High Street, Upwood, nr Ramsey. Tel: (01487) 813384

Location : village centre, 2 miles south-west of Ramsey.
Credit cards : not accepted.
Bitters : Directors, John Smith's, Courage Keg.
Plus Chestnut Mild, Beamish, Guinness.
Lagers : Holsten Export, Fosters. Plus Scrumpy Jack cider.

Examples from lunch menu (daily except Mons): *homemade steak & kidney-in-ale pie (noted); steak & stilton pie; lasagne; chicken cordon bleu; sweet & sour chicken; curry; scampi; cod; vegetable bake; venison & rabbit pie; omelettes; jacket potatoes; ploughman's; sandwiches. Trad. Sun. roasts £5.95 (2 courses).*

Examples from evening menu (daily): *8, 16, 24 or 32oz rump steaks; steaks in sauces; chicken with prawns & lobster; halibut & smoked salmon Wellington; char sui turkey steak; sizzlers eg beef teryaki; mushroom/courgette lasagne; vegetable pie.*

The examples above are only a cross-section from a huge and diverse menu; there are around nine vegetarian choices on the evening menu alone. Also a nice cross-section is the clientele - there's always a friendly, unhurried atmosphere. Even when empty the bar is warm, cosy and immaculate, but maybe not unoccupied: an old lady reportedly stoked the fire one Burns' Night and promptly vanished! There has been an inn on the site since Norman times, but this one dates from the 17th century, as can be guessed fom the old beams and open fires. Terra cotta flooring and wooden settles are nicely complemented by lots of brass and copper, and flowers on each table in the restaurant. This serves also for private parties, wedding receptions etc. Bob and Helga Martin, licensees since 1990, extend a warm welcome (children included) and have a play area in the garden. Darts and cards are indoor diversions, and there are plenty of good walks around this pleasant village.

THE LAZY OTTER

Cambridge Road, Stretham, nr Ely. Tel & Fax: (01353) 649780

Location: in lay-by off east side of A10, 1½ miles south of Stretham.
Credit cards: Access, Visa, Amex, Diners, Switch, Delta.
Bitters: Greene King (incl. seasonal specials), Marston's Pedigree, 2 guests.
Lagers: Carling, Fosters, Kronenbourg.

Examples from lunch menu (daily, plus evenings in bar): *fish & chips; grills/steaks; lasagne; cannelloni verdi; scampi; burgers; vegetarian orchard steak; ploughman's; baps; daily specials. Children's menu. Trad. Sun. roasts plus alternatives.*

Examples from evening restaurant menu (daily): *apple & cidered pork; lush chicken (with almonds, cream & Amaretto); steaks & grills; poached fillet of cod bonne femme; daily specials eg spicy spring rolls, braised steak, moussaka; home-made apple & peach pie.*

NB: OPEN ALL DAY in summer; all year Mon - Fri 12 to 3pm, 6 to 10pm; Sat 12 to 10pm, Sun 12 to 9pm (incl. food).

Hurtling past on the A10, one would barely suspect that such a fine river aspect lies just out of sight. But it can be enjoyed in all its glory from the conservatory dining room (or indeed the picnic tables) of this popular family-oriented pub, formerly a toll-house, with its own lagoon and moorings. The large garden has play equipment, and inside some tables are inlaid with snakes and ladders - a nice touch which indicates that youngsters are welcome. There is very much the feel of the country house: polished wood, bookshelves, ornate fireplace, although the atmosphere is anything but formal, especially on Wednesdays - live music night. Stephen and Lesley Owen are your amicable hosts.

THE BELL INN

Kennett, nr Newmarket. Tel: (01638) 750286

Location : crossroads B1506/B1085 (on old A45).
Credit cards : Access, Visa.
Accommodation : singles, twins & doubles - phone for details.
Bitters : Greene King Abbot & IPA, Rayments, Marstons Pedigree, Burtons, Websters, Tetley, guests.
Lagers : Kronenbourg, Carlsberg, Harp.

Examples of bar/restaurant meals (lunch & evening, 7 days): *prawn & crabmeat cocktail; breaded mushrooms with garlic dip; selection of daily fresh fish; steaks; mixed grill; half roast duck/chicken; porc a la creme; h/m steak & kidney pie; beef stroganoff; tagliatelle with ham & mushrooms in creamy sauce with herbs & garlic; mushroom & cashew strogonoff; devilled vegetables; omelettes; salads; ploughman's; sandwiches. H/m crumbles; spotted dick; treacle tart; pavlova. Trad. Sun. roasts.*

Literally straddling the border between Cambridgeshire and Suffolk, just outside that Mecca of the racing world, Newmarket, this solidly-built Tudor inn is well placed as a base for most of the region's principal towns and attractions; Bury St Edmunds and Cambridge are both an easy run. It is perhaps for this reason that it was once the haunt of highwaymen, and their hiding hole in the attic still exists. The clientele these days is eminently more respectable, but the bulding itself has changed little and is still graced by great oak beams and huge open fires. Bedrooms are clean, cosy and well equipped. The Smith family has considerable experience of running successful pubs, and The Bell is a 'firm favourite', not just with the racing punters but anyone who appreciate fresh, homecooked food on a daily changing menu.

Who's the vegetarian 'hanging around' in the restaurant?

THE RED LION FREEHOUSE

High Street, Hinxton, nr Cambridge. Tel: (01799) 530601, Fax: (01799) 531201

Location : vilage centre.
Credit cards : Access, Visa.
Bitters : Adnams, Bass, Boddingtons, Greene King IPA.
Lagers : Carling, Tennents.

Examples of bar/restaurant meals (lunch & evening, 7 days): *deep-fried mini camembert in gooseberry sauce; stilton & white port paté; Mediterranean prawns in garlic butter. Whitby Bay scampi; swordfish steak; roast duck bigarade with orange & Grand Marnier sauce; rainbow trout stuffed with prawns; steaks; Thai 10-veg. curry; leek & mushroom pie; many blackboard specials eg curry, chilli, lasagne, Newmarket sausage with onion gravy, salmon & broccoli quiche, tuna & pasta bake, mushroom & cashew nut stroganoff. Toffee meringue gateau; jam roly poly; spotted dick; pecan & maple syrup tart. Trad. Sun. roasts plus alternatives.*

Just a short detour off the M11 will take you to this very pleasant village with its handsome 16th-century coaching inn. Rated highly by a leading national good pub guide, food is home-cooked by a talented chef (vegetarians will be well pleased), and all is spotlessly clean and most inviting - why do people use plastic roadside eateries? It's also near enough to Cambridge to combine with a day's shopping or sightseeing, and would break up a journey from Norfolk to London very nicely. The tasteful restaurant extension is available for functions, and there's also a small drinking bar. Staff include George, an Amazonian parrot who likes to engage visitors in conversation, and a goat and pony in the garden. Their bosses are Jim and Lynda Crawford, now in their 12th year.

THE CHEQUERS INN

Fowlmere, nr Royston. Tel: (01763) 208369

Location: village centre.
Credit cards: Access, Visa, Diners, Amex, Switch.
Bitters: Tolly Cobbold, Tetleys.
Lagers: Carlsberg, Lowenbrau.

Examples of bar meals (lunch & evening, 7 days): *button mushrooms in garlic butter, wine, cream & tarragon; warm salad of bacon & prawns served with garlic bread; red Thai-style beef curry on basmati rice, with home-made pickles & chutney; selection of Irish cheeses with walnut bread.*

Examples of restaurant meals (as above): *Mediterranean dish of langoustines, squid, scallops, mussels & red mullet in shrimp sauce; roast partridge on green lentil sauce; home-made butter puff pastry case filled with spinach & creamed wild mushrooms. Mrs Beaton's bread & butter pudding with vanilla ice cream & strawberries; rich date sponge on sticky toffee sauce. Trad. Sun. roasts.*

For a small village Fowlmere has a lot of pubs, but The Chequers is easily the most celebrated, highly rated by all the major national guides and attracting trade from many miles around. The examples above suggest why this is so: food is of an exceptionally high order, a blend of the innovative and the familiar, all creatively prepared and presented. The 16th-century coaching inn itself is quite a draw, the galleried restaurant being the most noteworthy feature, and a crackling fire in winter. A conservatory may be used for functions, private parties etc., and overlooks the very pleasant garden where one may dine in summer. Freshly squeezed orange juice is a boon to drivers and the health-conscious, and there's also an outstanding choice of malt whiskies. Norman and Pauline Rushton, owners for over 14 years, welcome children.

THE PLOUGH

Coton, nr Cambridge. Tel: 01954 210489

Location: village centre, few minutes off M11.
Credit cards: Access, Visa, Diners, Amex.
Bitters: Flowers, Boddingtons, weekly guest.
Lagers: Stella Artois, Heineken.

Examples of bar meals (lunch & evening, 7 days): *steak & pitta bread; steak & kidney pudding; moussaka; lasagne, chilli; scampi; ploughman's; jacket potatoes; sandwiches; 3-course daily specials eg cream of mushroom soup, spaghetti carbonara, profiteroles with butterscotch sauce.*

Examples of restaurant meals (as above): *smoked salmon & asparagus terrine; parma ham with melon. Roast fillet of pork in Pernod & fennel sauce; roast brace of quail; chicken piri-piri; poached salmon with peach coulis; honey-glazed baked trout; garden bake. Chocolate, pear & Cointreau flan; spotted dick; treacle pud. Trad. Sun. roasts.*

Trained at Gleneagles, chef-proprietor John Williams acquired this 16th-century inn as recently as August 1995. Having worked here before, he was alert to the changes needed and has wasted no time in carrying them out, with many more improvements in the pipeline. Despite his background, he is determined that food should not take over - drinkers will always be welcome. Value is also paramount: OAP's can enjoy a three-course meal for just £4.45 on Thursdays (lunch & evening), and anybody can enjoy a three-course dinner with wine for only £8.95 from Monday to Wednesday (booking essential). Children (very welcome) have a games room with pool and SKY TV, plus play equipment in the large garden. Small weddings and parties up to 150 catered for. A nice foot/cycle path leads to nearby Trinity College - customers may leave the car at the pub.

*How many angels can
you fit on a horseback?*

THE WHITE HORSE INN

Swavesey, nr Cambridge. Tel: (01954) 230239

Location: on village square.
Credit cards: Mastercard, Visa.
Bitters: Boddingtons, Flowers IPA, Old Speckled Hen, occasional guests.
Lagers: Stella Artois, Heineken.

Examples of bar meals (lunch & evening, 7 days): *steak & kidney pie (prize-winning); chicken & almond fricassée; special curries; game pie; steaks; poached salmon steak; battered cod & chips; Julie's cheese & broccoli hot pot; mushroom & cashew nut casserole; Fenland smoked fish paté; deep-fried courgettes; jacket potatoes; omelettes; ploughman's; sandwiches. Home-made apple & blackberry pie; traditional pudding of the day; speciality ice creams. Trad. Sun. roasts.*

Aspiring publicans come here to learn the ropes; the school has won the National Innkeeping Award for Training. Their tutor is landlord and ex-brewer Anthony Stockbridge; he and landlady Marlene (former wine merchant) have won other accolades in their four years here, including a place in the top three nationally for steak & kidney pie, and in Wales and Central England for the curries. But all the food is home-made from fresh, local ingredients. The wine list is also exceptional and very modestly priced. For details of special nights ask to go on the mailing list. Tastefully refurbished, this early 17th-century inn is regarded as 'unthreatening' by unaccompanied ladies, and the dining room is no-smoking, but the Village Bar (once a courtroom and with a Tudor fireplace) is more traditionally 'pubby'. Pool room and darts. Well-behaved children welcome. Garden. Easy parking on lovely village square.

THE TRINITY FOOT

Huntingdon Road, Swavesey. Tel: (01954) 230315

Location: A14 (formerly A604) Eastbound, 7 miles west of Cambridge.
Credit cards: Access, Visa, Mastercard.
Bitters: Flowers, Boddingtons, Whitbreads.
Lagers: Stella Artois, Heineken.

Examples of bar meals (lunchtime 7 days, every evening except Sunday): *fresh fish at most times; fresh lobster from tank; samphire in season; queen scallops mornay; oysters au gratin; tiger prawns in garlic butter; John Dory; guinea fowl in red wine sauce; grilled mackerel Portuguese style; monkfish with Pernod & cream; steaks; mixed grill; curry; omelettes; salads. Sherry trifle; meringues glace; banana split; peach melba. Seasonal daily specials eg samphire, lobster, crab.*

Seafood is much more in evidence since the pub acquired its own fish shop, supplied from Lowestoft, Humberside and Loch Fyne. Also unusual, unique in fact, is the name Trinity Foot, after a pack of beagle hounds mastered by Colonel Whitbread, whose family's beer is on sale here. The hunters eschewed the usual fox as quarry, preferring hares, sportingly pursued on foot. 'Trinity' of course refers to the nearby university college. John and Brenda Mole will serve you delicious freshly prepared food in portions to satisfy the most ardent trencherman, with special evenings like French, Spanish or Portuguese to add a little zest. Well-behaved children are welcome in the eating area or unleashed onto the large, safe lawn, and there's also a conservatory. Despite its proximity to the A14, traffic is high up on an embankment and is not too intrusive. Large car park. Featured in national good pub guides.

THE WHITE HART INN

56 The Highway, Gt Staughton. Tel: (01480) 860345

Location : village centre, on B645.
Credit cards : not accepted.
Accommodation : in nearby guesthouse; 2 sngls, 3dbls/twins; tel. pub for details.
Bitters : Bass, Tetleys, Caffreys, guest.
Lagers : Stella Artois, Carlsberg.

Examples of bar meals (9AM TO 10:30PM EVERY DAY): *home-made soups (speciality) eg Jack's Hat (local wild mushrooms); steaks & grills; steak & stout pie; cod; scampi; all-day breakfast (£2.85); daily specials eg salmon en croute, chicken in stilton sauce. Home-made apple pie; bread & butter pudding; treacle pud; jam pud; spotted dick; chocolate pud. Trad. Sun. roasts (main course £4.15).*

Here is a straightforward, unpretentious village pub, serving wholesome traditional pub fare (mostly home-made and served in bar or small cottagey dining room) all day and every day at prices which many might have expected never to see again: starters at £1.65, for example. Consequently the 'Kelly Clan' have quickly won over the locals, and many a weary traveller, since taking over this 400-year-old coaching inn in Sept. '95. It seems there are one or two more longstanding members of the household who move things and make unearthly sounds. If the log fire in the inglenook doesn't drive them away then perhaps the Karaoke will - disco and quiz nights are also held in the Games Room, which has a sturdy pool table, skittles and darts; the courtyard has petanque and barbecue. Children and dogs welcome. Grafham Water just up the road.

THE EATON OAK

Crosshall Road, Eaton Ford, St Neots. Tel: (01480) 219555, Fax: (01480) 407520

Location : at junction of A1 with B645.
Credit cards : Mastercard, Visa, Eurocard, Amex.
Accommodation : 9 dbls/twins. All en suite, phone, satellite TV, tea & coffee.
Bitters : Charles Wells Eagle, Fargo & Bombardier.
Lagers : Red Stripe, McEwans.

Examples of bar meals (lunch & evening, 7 days): *chicken breast with stilton & bacon wrapped in puff pastry; steak au poivre; minted lamb steak; curry; chilli; lasagne; steak & kidney pie; Covent Garden pie; veg. tikka masala; oak-smoked haddock poached in milk & butter; ploughman's; sandwich*es.

Examples of restaurant meals (as above): *crispy coated brie in orange sauce; Japanese prawns; smoked seafood platter; steaks & grills; Cajun chicken; fresh fish; salmon en croute. Pear William shortcake; summer fruit pudding; apple strudel; rasp-berry meringue surprise. Trad. Sun. roasts.*

NB: Food available ALL DAY SUNDAY.

Charles Wells Brewery prefers its managed houses to be individual rather than formu-laic; being family-run, this one is no exception. Value and quality are the watchwords; food is freshly prepared and chalked daily on a blackboard. This former 18th-century farmhouse has been refurbished in style: thick carpeting and upholstery, wood pan-elling, brick arches, quality prints. The conservatory restaurant (available for functions) is especially attractive, with its small elevated 'galleries'. The normal laid-back atmosphere gives way now and again to live jazz, quiz nights and special occasions such as New Year and Beaujolais Evening. Well appointed accommodation is in a separate block, is well placed for local attractions like Grafham Water, and is only one hour from London. Children welcome. Small patio to front.

What did Edward Fitzgerald do gloriously in the fireplace?

THE FALCON INN

Rushden Road, Bletsoe, nr Bedford. Tel: (01234) 781222

Location : on A6 just south of village, towards Bedford.
Credit cards : Access, Visa, Eurocard, Switch.
Bitters : Chas Wells Eagle, Bomardier, Fargo, guest.
Lagers : McEwans, Red Stripe.

Examples of bar meals (lunch & evening, 7 days): *steak & Guinness pie; Cajun chicken breast; chilli; vegetarian lasagne; steaks; scampi; jacket potatoes; ploughman's; daily specials eg Yorkshire pudding with beef & onion gravy, grilled plaice, garlic chicken breast. White chocolate experience; apricot bavoir; tiramisu.*

Examples of restaurant meals (every evening, plus trad. Sun. lunch): *avocado & crab-meat mayonnaise; steaks; venison bourgignonne; salmon with herb & lime butter; honey roast chicken; broccoli & cream cheese bake; fresh seafood.*

Under new management since October '95, this 17th-century coaching inn must be unique in having a 300-acre estate behind it, in which is not only a three-mile stretch of Grade A fishing rights by the river (day tickets for sale), but also a large private lake full of carp. The small function room commands superb views over it all. Inside is also easy on the eye: low beams, a huge inglenook, brick floors, oak settles and an atmospheric oak-panelled restaurant (once a courthouse, which perhaps explains the strange footsteps and doors opening of their own accord!). All meat is butchered on the premises and freshly cooked; there are plans to introduce more seafood, pig roasts in the garden and special promotions, as well as honouring red-letter days. Well-behaved children welcome. Skittles and darts. Country Park nearby.

145

THE BELL

Horsefair Lane, Odell. Tel: (01234) 720254

Location : village centre.
Credit cards : not accepted.
Bitters : Greene King.
Lagers : Harp, Kronenbourg.

Examples of bar meals (lunch & evening, 7 days): *venison casserole; spinach, bacon & cream cheese roulade; creamy fish, mushroom & broccoli pie; shepherds pie; steak & kidney pie; turkey, leek & mushroom pie; chicken kiev. Boozy chocolate mousse; pecan nut pie; whisky ginger cream; pineapple raisin cheesecake.*

It looks every inch the ideal thatched country pub, and for once appearances are not deceiving. Tucked away in a quiet village not far from Odell Country Park, its 16th-century origins are apparent from the superb inglenook and exposed beams in the five rather cosy bar areas. One may eat anywhere (including the patio) and be sure of good, home-cooked food, prepared by the landlady herself, Doreen Scott. She and husband Derek have, over the past 10 years, earned the respect of the major national guides and local people, who appreciate the friendly atmosphere and absence of wailing juke-boxes etc. Children have an area set aside for them but will be sure to head for the little river which tumbles past the end of the garden (when not in drought!).

THE MAGPIES

Bedford Street, Woburn. Tel: (01525) 290219

Location : on main street, town centre.
Credit cards : not accepted.
Accommodation : 8 dbls/twins; 1 en suite, all with TV, tea & coffee.
From £25 - £45 per room.
Bitters : Marston's Pedigree, Ruddles.
Lagers : Carlsberg, Fosters, Holsten.

Examples from lunch menu (Mon - Sat, plus trad. Sun. roasts): *cannelloni stuffed with mushrooms & bacon; Mexican-style tacos; omelettes; jacket potatoes; BLT; filled French bread; daily specials eg curried pork, pasta tubes with spicy sausage.*

Examples from evening menu (Tues - Sat): *mixed pepper & cream cheese mousse with toasted ciabatta; warm chicken & leek tartlet; oriental noodle salad with prawns; boneless cod fillet with herb & lemon crust; grilled egg plant with sweet pepper & tomato mille-feuille; tender breast of chicken with dried tomato & shallot sauce; daily specials eg kangaroo, wild boar. Glazed apple sponge with lemon custard; dark chocolate cheesecake; strawberry shortbread.*

Even without the famous Abbey and Safari Park nearby, Woburn is one of England's premier villages, its dignified and historic main street well worth a long drive. Be sure to include this hospitable, timbered, 16th-century coaching inn, restaurant-oriented but with a small, cosy bar, run personally by Sylvia and Len Beswick and family. Grandson-in-law Andrew is chef; he hails from down under, but his virtuosity extends well beyond the preparation of kangaroo! Value-for-money is also exceptional: Pasta Evenings on Tuesdays, for example, offer all you can eat for an amazing £3.95. Another favourite time to visit is at the Oyster Festival on the first Sunday of September - good idea to book a bedroom. Function room. Car park.

THE CROSS KEYS

High Street, Pulloxhill. Tel: (01525) 712442

Location : off A6 between Luton & Bedford.
Credit cards : Mastercard, Visa, Switch.
Bitters : Chas. Wells Fargo & Eagle, Adnams Broadside.
Lagers : McEwans, Red Stripe, Kellerbrau.

Examples of bar/restaurant meals (lunch & evening, 7 days): *fresh mushrooms in garlic butter; trout; steaks & grills; pork cordon bleu; lobster; roast duckling; salads; ploughman's; daily specials eg battered cod, hot & spicy pastie, deep-fried haddock in mornay sauce, duck in orange/cherry sauce. Home-made fruit pies; butterscotch ice cream with toffee chunks; Grandma's butter pecan. Trad. Sun. roasts.*

Acker Bilk, Kenny Baker, Charlie Galbraith and other famous jazz musicians enjoy playing here at the regular Sunday-night bash (entry free); like the customers, they appreciate the bonhomie and special atmosphere. This in part derives from the 15th-century building itself, but mostly it is due to the 25 years' stewardship of Peter and Sheila Meads and their long-serving staff. When they took over a pint of bitter was 7½d (old pence), soup was 1/6 and a steak 12/6! Today's prices still afford excellent value, a temptation to eat out more often. The 80 wines listed (clarets a speciality) are also modestly priced, and there are occasional wine-tasting evenings with food to match. The attractive restaurant (available for functions) overlooks 10 acres of grounds - room enough for a marquee, barbecue, cricket pitch, boules, pitch and putt and caravan park! Three-course (+ coffee) senior citizens' lunch £3.25 Mon - Fri.

THE KING'S ARMS

London Road, Sandy. Tel: (01767) 680276

Location : just off A1 near Bickerdike's Garden Centre.
Credit cards : Mastercard, Visa, Switch, Amex.
Accommodation : 4 dbls/twins in chalets. All en suite, TV, tea & coffee.
£30 per chalet, brkfst extra.
Bitters : Greene King, Rayments.
Lagers : Harp, Kronenbourg, Stell Artois.

Examples of bar meals (lunch & evening except Sun. evening): *home-made paté; beef casserole; home-made pie of the day; curry; steak; scampi; plaice; salads; plough-man's; sandwiches; jacket potatoes; daily specials eg beef korma, venison pie, Whitby haddies.*

Examples of restaurant meals (as above): *fillet stilton (speciality); pork Somerset; beef stroganoff; lamb Wellington; grilled Dover sole; fillet of salmon in asparagus sauce; venison steak with cranberry sauce; cashew nut balls; spinach & ricotta cheese can-nelloni. Trad. Sun. roasts.*

The many admirers (including major national guides) of Ken and Jean Parry during their 13 years at The Mad Dog, Little Odell, should note that they are now resident pro-prietors of this warm, characterful and refurbished 17th-century coaching inn on the old Gt North Road. As ever, they offer "sustenance and shelter" to the weary traveller, in the form of a wide range of chef-prepared food, good wines and ales, and very affordable accommodation, well suited to business people or visitors to RSPB, Old Warden Aerodrome and Swiss Gardens. A small function room takes up to 14 people. Children are welcome in the dining room up to 8pm; the garden has a barbecue and two petanque courts.

149

What is the shortest distance for the Swiss from Ireland?

THE HARE & HOUNDS
Old Warden, nr Bedford. Tel: (01767) 627225

Photo courtesy Dave Hillyard

Location : village high street (2 miles from A1).
Credit cards : Mastercard, Visa, Switch, JCB.
Accommodation : in nearby guesthouse - arrange through pub.
Bitters : Five on draught, always rotating.
Lagers : Red Stripe, McEwans.

Examples of bar meals (lunch & evening, 7 days; OPEN FOR FOOD ALL DAY AND EVERY DAY UP TO 11PM IN SUMMER): *sesame prawn toasts with seafood dip; large French-style omelettes; steak & kidney pie; country pie; cod; scampi; lasagne; steaks; orange & cream turkey; lime & ginger chicken; rosemary & garlic lamb; veg. flan; daily specials eg fresh steamed fish, lamb curry, burgers in onion sauce for vegetarians. 'Serious' chocolate cake; fruit crumbles; syrup sponge; spotted dick; super ice creams; light bread & butter pudding. Traditional Sunday roasts.*

Here is a village to dispel any notion that Bedfordshire has nothing worth turning off the A1 for. The eye is met with a 'stage-set' vision of thatched 18th-century cottages clustered in a fold in the rolling countryside, backed by a wonderful treeline. It is also home to one of the county's better pubs, under new family ownership since spring 1995. With many years' experience garnered in Berkshire, their philosophy is that this is not a restaurant selling beer, but a pub selling food. The latter is home-cooked and served in platefuls, but drinkers are always welcome; no more than half the tables may be reserved and the atmosphere is very informal throughout the four bars, each with a charm of its own (one celebrates the life of aviator Richard Shuttleworth - the famous Shuttleworth Collection and Swiss Gardens are very nearby). By the time you read this, there should be a splendid sheltered courtyard in the large garden. Family room.

THE BLACK HORSE
Ireland, nr Shefford. Tel: (01462) 811398

Location : off A600, 1 mile from Shefford towards Bedford.
Credit cards : not accepted.
Bitters : Bass, Worthington, Shepherd Neame Spitfire.
Lagers : Carling, Tennents Extra.

Examples from lunch menu (daily except Mondays): *home-made steak & kidney pie; roast loin of lamb; liver & bacon; chicken fillet Frederick; Mexican cheese & pasta bake; scampi; plaice. Trad. Sun. roasts.*

Examples from evening menu (daily except Mondays): *pork steak Normand; entrecote steak brie; half crispy roast duck; supreme of chicken Caribbean; lamb steak Barnett; poached natural haddock; lobster thermidor; grilled skate. Fresh fish night on Thursdays.*

NB: pub is closed all day Mondays.

This is one Ireland you can reach without crossing the water (unless you count the River Ivel). The odd name is a corruption of the original 'Highland'. Built around 300 years ago in the heart of the Whitbread Estate, it stands on high ground in pleasant rolling countryside. Also elevated is the standard of food, further augmented on theme nights, such as Thai or Suckling Pig. As the photo shows, the display of hanging baskets is stunning. There's also a well kept garden with swings, but inside is very agreeable too: oak-beamed, with open fires and a separate dining room. Roy and Gordon, with wives Pam and Jean, have been the cordial hosts for over eight years. Pool table. Shuttleworth, Swiss Garden and Old Warden Aerodrome (airshows and veteran cars) all nearby.

151

THE FOX & DUCK

Arlesey Road, Stotfold, nr Hitchin. Tel: (01462) 732434

Location : on A507 west of Stotfold.
Credit cards : Mastercard, Visa, Switch, Delta, Eurocard.
Bitters : Chas Wells IPA, Youngs Special, Boddingtons, 3 guests.
Lagers : Red Stripe, Fosters, McEwans, Kellerbrau.

Examples from lunch menu (daily): *tagliatelle carbonara; leek, cheese & potato bake; chicken Kiev; gammon; jacket potatoes; ploughman's (noted); sandwiches; daily specials eg lasagne, home-made pies. Children's meals £3.50 incl. ice cream. Trad. Sun. roasts £7.95 incl. sweet (booking strongly advised).*

Examples from evening menu (daily): *fresh mussels; cheesy garlic fresh mushrooms; liver, bacon & onions; king ribs; steaks; steak & kidney pie; chicken & mushroom pie; broccoli & cream cheese bake; ratatouille lasagne; daily specials eg fresh fish (sometimes exotic), lamb Italienne, fresh scampi Pernod, Mexican chicken. Spotted dick; home-made apple pie; fresh fruit salad. (Booking advised Sat. evenings)*

NB: OPEN ALL DAY SUNDAYS FOR FOOD

In a heartening reversal of current trends, the Aisthorpe family - Nigel and Pat (known to friends as Basil and Sybil), daughter Lucy and Giles - have turned this 200-year-old roadside pub from a derelict ruin into one of the region's rising stars. A wide spectrum of customers beat a path for the generous portions of home cooking, well kept ales and a warm greeting from the staff and two log fires. Freshly-squeezed orange juice is another nice touch. The separate dining room (functions up to 50) is no-smoking, and patio doors open onto the garden. The family were pioneers of the Senior Citizen's Lunch, and still offer two courses for just £3.25 every Wednesday. Sinful ladies returning home from nearby Henlow Grange indulge themselves here after a week's good behaviour! Children welcome.

THE TUDOR OAKS LODGE & RESTAURANT

Taylors Road, Astwick. Tel & Fax: (01462) 834133

Location : west side of A1; from the north take the Astwick exit and turn immediately left into narrow lane.

Credit cards : Access, Visa, Amex, Diners.

Accommodation : 1 sngl (£36 incl., £30 at weekends), 8 dbls/twins (£45, £35 at weekends). All en suite, TV, phone, hair dryer, trouser press, mini bar; 1 with 4-poster & jacuzzi.

Bitters : Courage Directors, Fullers London Pride, Boddingtons, many unusual guests (300+ in '95).

Lagers : Stella Artois, Red Stripe. Plus real ciders & perry.

Examples of bar meals (lunch & evening, 7 days): *home-made curries: steak & kidney pie; chicken & ham pie; pork with apple in cider pie; steaks; omelettes; mushroom stroganoff; ploughman's; many daily specials eg toad-in-the-hole, whole grilled sea bass, trucker's breakfast, Chicago ribs.*

Examples of restaurant meals (as above): *steak Tudor Oaks (with light cream & prawn sauce); chicken Valdostana (breast with ham, cheese, mushroom & tomatoes); grilled Dover sole; trout amandine. Trad. Sun. roasts. Senior Citizens' lunches £2.75 Mon-Fri.*

Literally on the border with Herts, this 15th-century coaching inn, shamefully derelict until 1978, has been restored to former glory, retaining the original oak beams and hand-made red bricks. On the upper of the two-tier bar comfortable Chesterfields sit in front of a huge fireplace. Upstairs is the heavily timbered and cottagey restaurant. There's monthly live entertainment in the night club, and discos Thursday to Saturday evenings. The well equipped bedrooms are in chalets around a pretty courtyard. The chef patron's high standards - all food is fresh and prepared on the premises - continue to earn a place in leading national guides. Conferences and parties catered for.

THE ROSE & CROWN

69 High Street, Ashwell, nr Baldock. Tel: (01462) 742420

Location: village centre.
Credit cards: Visa, Mastercard, Eurocard.
Bitters: Greene King.
Lagers: Harp, Kronenbourg.

Examples from lunch menu (daily): *fresh baked fish of the day; steak in ale pie; chicken & leek au gratin; salmon & prawn pancake; baked avocado topped with melted cheese; club sandwiches; ploughman's; daily specials. Bread & butter pudding; treacle tart; fruit crumble. Trad. Sun. roasts.*

Examples from evening menu (Tues - Sun): *chargrilled tuna fillet; medallions of venison in portwine & redcurrant sauce; fillet of beef stroganoff; sole fillet rolled with crabmeat & scallops; pasta Florentine; breast of chicken pan-fried with melted stilton & apricots.*

NB: Tuesdays & Thursdays are fresh fish & chip days.

A regular in national good pub guides, this 15th-century coaching inn could nevertheless not be described as a 'foodie' pub. The menu is exceptionally tempting, but you are just as welcome if you are just looking for a quiet, unhurried pint and good conversation in a convivial atmosphere. At least one soul is apparently reluctant to depart, lingering on in spirit form. The bar is divided into four cosy areas, one set aside for games and another with a magnificent inglenook fireplace. Children are welcome in eating areas and the very well kept garden to the rear of the car park. Ashwell is one of Hertfordshire's more picturesque villages.

*Which former owner inoculated
a great queen?*

THE RISING SUN

Halls Green, Weston, nr Baldock. Tel: (01462) 790487

Location : turn into Maiden Street by duck pond in Weston village centre;
follow this road for approx. 2 miles.

Credit cards : Mastercard, Visa.

Bitters : McMullens, Courage Directors, Bass, occasional guest.

Lagers : Hartsman, Stella Artois, Fosters.

Examples of bar meals (lunch & evening, 7 days): *deep-fried mushrooms with dips; mussels in garlic butter; shellfish platter; home-made chilli; lasagne; steak & kidney pie; fish pie; steaks & grills; vegetable curry; spicy bean hotpot; ploughman's; chunky sandwiches; daily specials eg Szechaun pork, fresh crab, rogon josh, spare ribs. Children's menu. Trad. Sun. roasts.*

"I'm a publican who likes to serve food, not a restaurateur" - the words are Tony Szpak's, who, after long experience in the trade, came to this former 18th-century cottage about three years ago with wife Jennie. It's a lovely spot in good walking or cycling country, but is well off the beaten track, so to flourish they must offer something special, and indeed they do. Food is wholesome, generous and very reasonably priced, accompanied by an interesting wine list, also most affordable, and may be enjoyed in a very pleasant conservatory dining area. For extra sparkle look out for theme nights (usually on Wednesdays), such as Beuajolais, Far Eastern, Chinese or Welsh. It's also a great place to take the family: in the vast acres of grounds are a five-a-side pitch, play area, tuck shop, barbecue, petanque and pony (and trap) rides in summer! Bar billiards is the indoor sport. Knebworth, Cromer Windmill, Lamark Pottery all nearby. Parties and business lunches catered for, or just call in for a casual drink!

THE LYTTON ARMS

Park Lane, Old Knebworth. Tel: (01438) 812312

Location : mid-way between Knebworth and Codicote.
Credit cards : Access, Visa, Diners, Amex.
Bitters : 13 real ales - Bass, Theakstons, Woodfordes Wherry, guests.
Lagers : Carling, Tennents, Warsteiner. Plus 50 Belgian bottled.

Examples of bar meals (lunch & evening, 7 days): *smoked fish platter; dim sum; jalapos; steaks & grills; home-made steak & mushroom (in ale) pie; lasagne; chilli; balti; speciality sausages; plaice, scampi; jacket potatoes; ploughmans; sandwiches; daily specials eg spinach & ricotta canelloni; veg. lasagne; sweet & sour chicken; nasi goreng. Home-made fruit crumble; jam roly poly; spotted dick; treacle & nut tart. Cheese or meat fondues for groups of 4-12.*

Knebworth House is one of the grandest and most visited stately homes in the land, and this traditional 19th-century country pub is part of the Lytton family estate - old photos of house and family form part of the decor. The countryside in these parts is very pleasant - ideal for ramblers and cyclists - and after stretching the legs and filling the lungs there's good, wholesome food to look forward to, as well as an outstanding choice of beer (winning plaudits from CAMRA) and 50 malt whiskies. Barbecues are held in the garden (with patio) in summer, which also has play facilities for children. Proprietor Stephen Nye is now in his eighth year here. Large car park.

THE GEORGE & DRAGON

High Street, Watton-at-Stone. Tel: (01920) 830285

Location : village centre, between Stevenage & Hertford.
Credit cards : Access, Visa, Diners, Amex.
Bitters : Greene King. Plus Guinness & Murphy's stout.
Lagers : Harp, Kronenbourg, Stella Artois.

Examples of bar/restaurant meals (lunch & evening, except Sun. evening): *Corsican fish soup; Greek salad with fresh oregano & basil; cornets of smoked salmon filled with fresh salmon & chive mousse; chicken breast stuffed with cream cheese & grapes on white wine & cream sauce; pasta Roberto (mix of red lentils, spinach, basil, garlic & cheese); George & Dragon fish stew; millionaire's or billionaire's bun (depending on size of fillet steak filling); boboeti (hot & spicy minced beef curry); salads; plough-man's; sandwiches; chalkboard specials which nearly always include fresh fish. Home-made puddings.*

"The pub with the club atmosphere" is a fair description. Built as a pub in 1603, it exudes an air of comfort and well being, with its old beams, antique furniture and prints, and fresh flowers in abundance. To relax by the log fire with the papers (provided) and good food and drink is a simple but profound pleasure. But it is not only the warm hospitality which has secured a regular place - indeed a star rating - in the national guides; as a glance over the examples above will suggest, the cooking is of a high order and uncommonly original. Occasional special nights add further interest and the wine list is always excellent. Children welcome as far as facilities will allow, but there is a newly extended garden and patio. Ample parking.

THE BULL

113 High Street, Watton-at-Stone. Tel: (01920) 831032

Location : on main road through village.
Credit cards : Mastercard, Visa, Amex.
Bitters : Greene King, McMullens, Burton, Tetley.
Lagers : Carlsberg, Castlemaine.

Examples of bar/restaurant meals (lunch & evening, 7 days): *spicy potato wedges with barbecue sauce; prawn & pineapple brochette; chicken satay; chicken balti; chicken tikka masala; curry; chilli; barbecue spare ribs; steaks & grills; tuna & pasta florentine; liver & bacon; beef stroganoff; crispy veg. parcels; mushroom balti with naan; baguettes; ploughman's; sandwiches; daily specials eg salmon with cheese & herb sauce, grilled plaice. Rhubarb crumble; mincemeat bakewell; profiteroles; treacle sponge; spotted dick; toffee apple & pecan pie. Children's menu. Trad. Sun. roasts.*

The magnificent fireplace, lit in winter, is the first feature to catch the eye, but it is what is on the blackboard which makes this 15th-century coaching inn especially noteworthy and popular. It lists a wide diversity of choice, freshly home-made, with Indian dishes well represented as well as time-honoured English favourites. Look out for special evenings (usually Mondays), when the theme might be Curry, Italian or Chinese cooking, for example. You may like to enjoy it in the cosy dining room (available also for functions), where you could also find the answer to the 'trivia' question. Tuesday evenings see the large, characterful bar become the stage for live music. Experienced proprietors Mike and Bev Morris welcome children and have a play area, menagerie and barbecue in the garden. Large car park. Knebworth and Hatfield Houses not far.

THE SOW & PIGS

Cambridge Road, Thundridge, nr Ware. Tel: (01920) 463281

Location: on west side of A10, 3 miles north of Ware.
Credit cards: Access, Visa, Mastercard, Switch.
Bitters: Adnams, Shipstones, Wadworth 6X, Tetley.
Lagers: Labatts, Stella Artois, Carling.

Examples of bar meals (lunch & evening, 7 days): *home-made soup; mushrooms in cider & stilton sauce; melon fan & grenadine syrup; steak; duck breast in passion fruit & orange sauce; pork fillet in apple cream sauce; special grill; whole grilled plaice; mushroom & courgette stroganoff; sandwiches; ploughmans; daily specials eg vegetable balti, ham & mushroom pie, pork chop with mustard sauce, Yorkshire fish & chips & mushy peas. Trad. Sun. roasts.*

You won't feel like a stranger for long here; the staff are notably welcoming and proprietor (since June '95) Meriel Riches (formerly of next-door Hanbury Manor) is rarely to be seen on the 'business' side of the bar, preferring to rub shoulders with customers. If it's no surprise to find pig collections displayed everywhere, then the diversity of the many pieces certainly is. Apparently the name derives from a card game popular when the inn was built in 1592 to serve passing coaches. Pig roasts are a succulent seasonal treat, but the standard of food is always high, recognised by major national guides. All red-letter days are celebrated, and guest chefs are brought in for special theme evenings, such as Thai, Indian or Mexican. There is a separate dining room but a marquee in the garden serves for functions, wedding receptions etc. Activity box for children. No indoor games or piped music.

THE PLUME OF FEATHERS
Upper Green, Tewin. Tel: (01438) 717265

Location: edge of village, towards Burnham Green.
Credit cards: Access, Visa, Mastercard, Switch, Eurocard.
Bitters: Adnams, Marston's Pedigree, Bass, Caffreys, 5 guests.
Lagers: Stella Artois, Carling.

Examples of bar meals (lunch & evening, 7 days): *Thai seafood curry; fresh fish of the day; steak & kidney pudding; pork & leek sausages; tomato, pepper & pesto tart; daily specials eg sizzling duck. Amaretto parfait; home-made pear & almond vanilla icecream; chocolate mousse cake.*

Examples of restaurant meals (as above): *crispy duck; Covent Garden terrine; fresh calamari & octopus. Steaks; fillet of red mullet with slithered almonds & king prawns; pot-roasted local rabbit; venison sausages with juniper berries & apple; baked field mushrooms with fresh corn & diced peppers in pepper sauce. Trad. Sun. roasts.*

Four chefs use only fresh produce (incl. pasta) and a lot of verve to make this 16th-century alehouse (sister pub to The Bricklayers at Flaundon) one of the area's best loved places to eat. Being in a very select neighbourhood, you may also find yourself rubbing shoulders with 'celebs'. There was none bigger than QE I, who used it as a hunting lodge. A skilled refurbishment has restored many period features, but perhaps most unusual is the gallery, an opulent sitting room with Persian rug. The very attractive restaurant overlooks a two-acre garden (with sandpit, volleyball, boules and barbecue), which itself commands wonderful views over farmland - a great venue for a wedding reception (marquee available). Toilets for disabled; baby-changing facilities.

THE FIVE HORSESHOES
FREEHOUSE & RESTAURANT

1 Church Road, Little Berkhamsted, nr Hertford.
Tel: Cuffley (01707) 875055,Fax: (01707) 876315

Location : village centre, opp. cricket ground (not to be confused with Berkhamsted, some 30 miles away).
Credit cards : Access, Visa, Amex.
Bitters : Greene King, Ansells, McMullens.
Lagers : Lowenbrau, Castlemaine, Skol, Carlsberg.

Examples of bar meals (lunch & evening, 7 days): *grilled sardines in garlic butter; pork spare ribs with oriental sauces; vegetable curry; steak in ale pie; chilli; lasagne; sausage & mash; braised liver & bacon; steak; chicken chasseur; stuffed belly of pork; roasts; salads; sandwiches; jacket potatoes; vegetarian dishes. Apple crumble; spotted dick; banana & rum cheesecake.*

Examples of restaurant meals (lunch & evening, 7 days): *spiced soft roes on toast; stilton field mushrooms with herb crust & tomato sauce. Whole large orange tilapia (St Peter's fish) foil-baked with wine, lemon & lime; lamb loin with onion & garlic in puff pastry; half roast duckling with apple sauce; fabulous Scottish steaks; vegetarian dishes. 10% service charge.*

Few other pubs or restaurants have their own butchery. Taste the beef here and you will know the difference: it cuts like butter. Everything is home-prepared and fresh; meat is bought direct from the farm, fish daily from the market. It is this attention to quality which has given Ray Curson nine successful years at this 17th-century Grade II listed freehouse in one of Hertfordshire's most delightful villages. He also refurbished extensively, creating the fine galleried restaurant (available for private functions). Smart dress is appropriate here, but the characterful bars are quite informal. St George's Day, Burns Night and other special dates are always celebrated, and barbecues are held in the garden, weather permitting. Good wine list includes local Howe Green vineyard. Ample parking. Customer mailing list.

THE CRICKETERS

The Green, Sarratt. Tel: (01923) 263729

Location : on village green, 2 miles off jncn 18 of M25.
Credit cards : Access, Visa, Amex.
Bitters : Courage, guest.
Lagers : Fosters, Kronenbourg.

Examples of bar/restaurant meals (lunch & evening, 7 days): *baked Basque fish; chilli spiced cod & prawn casserole; swordfish steak; chicken, mandarin & brie pie; steak & kidney pie; lamb rogan josh; aubergine stuffed with vegetable risotto; speciality sausages; broccoli, cream cheese & vegetable pie; grills/steaks; salads; ploughmans; jacket potatoes; daily specials eg pan-fried medallions of tuna in soya & garlic glaze, barbecued pare ribs. Hazelnut roulade; tipsy whisky cake; fruit crumble. Trad. Sun. roasts (plus late afternoon sitting).*

NB: open all day - some cold food always available.

Although at the western extremity of the region, this lovely village is made very accessible by the M25. Yet it remains blissfully rural and unspoilt, just far enough away from the rumble of traffic, and with some fine country and riverside walks. Built around 350 years ago as three cottages, The Cricketers has long been a popular watering hole, but all the more so now there is the boon of all-day opening. At four o'clock on a sunny afternoon it is a quiet joy to sit by the large green next to the duck pond with a good pint and fresh salad, perhaps. With one or two necessary exceptions all the food is home-made and fresh. Barbecues are held in summer, there are monthly quiz nights and a dart board. A number of interesting developments are planned. Children welcome.

HOTELS & RESTAURANTS

THE CROWN RESTAURANT & BAR

56 Long Lane, Aston End, nr Stevenage. Tel: (01438) 880060

Hours : 12 to 3pm, 7 to 10:30pm, except Sun evenings & Mons.
Credit cards : Mastercard, Visa.
Price guide : set price £17.50 & £19.50 (2 & 3 courses);
lunch £11 & £13.50 (2 & 3 courses).

Examples from restaurant menus (revised daily): *ravioli of chicken & leeks with tarragon; terrine of aubergines, buffalo mozarella & red pepper. Fillet of Scotch salmon with herb crust, lemon sauce & mash; roast rack of lamb with a mustard, mint & green peppercorn crust; penne with gorgonzola spinach & peas. Terrine of chocolate with coffee bean sauce; banana, toffee & nut crumble with custard; strawberries with Greek yoghurt, honey & mint. Sunday roasts plus alternatives. Bar: Moroccan lamb with veg. stew; roast cod in mushroom & pesto; toasted goat's cheese with sun-dried tomatoes. Tapas Thursday evenings accompanied by live jazz or guitar.*

The name and outward appearance suggest, correctly, that this was once a pub (be sure not to confuse it with the Rose & Crown at nearby Aston). However, over the past two years or so chef proprietor Robert Armstrong has established the Crown as one of the county's leading restaurants, with imaginative English and Mediterranean cooking, a much needed boost to an area strangely lacking in gastronomic flair. Yet prices remain very good value for the quality. All is cooked to order (no freezer, no fryer) both in the bistro-style bar and the large, airy restaurant - flowers on each table, crisp linen, wooden floor, modern art and a pleasant outlook through the French windows over the landscaped garden. A marquee can take up to 500 for functions. Ask to go on the newsletter mailing list.

REDCOATS FARMHOUSE HOTEL

Redcoats Green, nr Hitchin. Tel: (01438) 729500, Fax: (01438) 723322

Hours : 12 to 1:30pm (daily except Sats), 7 to 9pm (daily except Suns).
Closed Bank Hols.
Credit cards : Access, Visa, Diners, Amex.
Price guide : a la carte £26; Club Lunch £13 & £15 (2 & 3 courses);
Supper Menu from £3.50; Sun. lunch £16.
Accommodation : 1 sngl, 13 dbls/twins; 12 en suite, TV, phone, hair dryer, tea & coffee.
£60 sngl, £70 dbl, weekend breaks from £90 for 2 nights dinner, b & b.

Examples from menus (revised fortnightly): *fresh scampi tails in garlic butter; home-made rabbit brawn with mustard pickle; roasted tomato salad with pinenuts & olives. Fresh hake cutlet au poivre; fillet steak topped with Guinness & cheddar; grouse served with fried breadrumbs & whisky gravy; casserole of mixed vegetables & pulses on wild rice. Home-made Toblerone & sherry ice cream; peach pudding with walnut & butterscotch sauce; savouries eg angels on horseback, Welsh rarebit. Trad. Sun. roasts.*

"Not so much an hotel, more a way of life" says owner Peter Butterfield. Remarkably, this 15th-century farmhouse (although now mostly Victorian) has been in his family since 1916. And it is homely, in the way that only a family-run business can be, with antiques and paintings, open fireplaces, exposed timbers and an attractive conservatory overlooking the 4-acre garden - with a marquee, a lovely location for a wedding reception. Tellingly, chef John Ruffle has worked here for over 15 years, and has earned consistent ratings in the major good food and hotel guides. Customers become devotees - most of the business is repeat bookings. Only minutes from the A1 and 35 miles from central London, this is nevertheless one of the more tranquil and picturesque parts of Hertfordshire.

THE LOBSTER TAIL
16 High Street, Gt Offley, nr Hitchin. Tel: (01462) 768391

Hours: 12 to 2pm Tues - Fri, 7 to 9:30pm Tues - Sat.
Credit cards: Access, Visa, Diners, Amex.
Price guide: a la carte £25.

Examples from menu (revised daily according to market): *Scotch smoked salmon; marinated seafood; chef's special paté; tricolore (veg.). Turbot with chablis sauce & prawns; red snapper in spicy Caribbean sauce; seafood thermidor; scallops meuniere; halibut on bed of spinach with mornay sauce; fillet steak chasseur; vegetable stroganoff. Creme Catalan brulée; chocolate parfait; oranges in caramel sauce flavoured with Grand Marnier.*

The very special appeal of fresh seafood is perhaps appreciated all the more by those who live far from the briney. The people of Hertfordshire continue to acclaim this is as one of the very best restaurants of any kind in the county since it opened over seven years ago. The provenance of Billingsgate, Lowestoft and Scotland is chalked up daily on a blackboard and prepared to order (and accompanied by a good wine list). Definitely not on the menu is Osphoremus Gaurami (Delilah to her friends), a large 12-year-old tropical fish in a tank. With intelligent interest she watches over this former 16th-century pub, very cottagey, with soft lighting, candles, flowers, pink and white linen, and a corner alcove for private parties. Gt Offley is a pleasant little village, not far from Knebworth, Whipsnade or Luton Hoo.

THE KNIFE & CLEAVER
Houghton Conquest, nr Bedford. Tel: (01234) 740387, Fax: (01234) 740900

Hours: 12 to 2:30pm, 7 to 9:30pm daily except Sun. evenings.
Credit cards: Access, Visa, Diners, Amex.
Price guide: a la carte £18-20; table d'hote £17.50 (3 courses);
lunch £11.95 (2 courses).
Accommodation: 9 dbls/twins (3 de luxe, 6 stndrd). All en suite, TV, phone, fridge,
hair dryer, tea & coffee. RAC 2*. From £45 sngl,
£59 dbl. Dbl at sngl rate weekends.

Examples from menus (revised monthly): *deep-fried fresh crabmeat & prawn fritters with lemon & sour cream dip; smoked pheasant & fennel sausage with baked fennel gratin; large h/m ravioli purse filled with pancetta, asparagus & parmesan. Monkfish with cucumber & vermouth sauce; baked loin of lamb with duxelle stuffing wrapped in pastry with mint-flavoured bearnaise sauce; tomato & red pepper summer pudding. Home-made desserts & outstanding cheese board. Bar: French fish soup; baguette filled with pan-fried fillet steak & smoked cheddar; mushroom brioche; some dishes as above. Trad. Sun. roasts.*

This is one of the county's most widely respected restaurants, established as such over six years by David and Pauline Loom, and one of the few where truly fresh fish (a speciality) may be enjoyed. The air-conditioned conservatory dining room (available for functions) is light and airy, and overlooks the flower-bedecked terrace. If eating informally, the bar is also very pleasant, with oak panelling (from nearby Houghton House), low beams and a feature fireplace. Every six weeks on a Friday is a special evening, eg Midsummer live jazz; or try a wine evening, such as Bordeaux, with food to match (ask to go on the mailing list). Spoil yourself with an overnight stay and relax over the papers and a hearty breakfast.

167

RUSSELL'S BRASSERIE

38 The Embankment, Bedford. Tel & Fax: (01234) 212848

Hours: 10am to 10pm, every day.
Credit cards: Mastercard, Visa, Diners, Amex.
Price guide: a la carte £14, snacks from £3.

Examples from menu (revised occasionally): *baked goats' cheese parcel dusted with pine nuts; home-cured salmon with dill sauce & pickled cucumber. Mexican pot; chicken breast stuffed with garlic cream cheese & spinach, wrapped in parma ham; duck breast in creamy green peppercorn sauce; salmon fishcakes in fresh tomato sauce; large seafood salad; chargrilled sirloin; vegetarian stuffed pancakes with cheese sauce; sandwiches & bagels; daily specials eg beef daube, trawler pie. Tarte tatin; creme brulée; bread & butter pudding. Breakfasts (until noon). Afternoon teas (3 to 6pm). Trad. Sun. roasts.*

Many of us lament our lack of continental-style brasseries, serving good food all day at affordable prices. But here is just such a place, in what is easily Bedford's most attractive quarter, a pleasant 15 minutes' tree-lined riverside promenade from the centre (turn left just before bridge). In high summer, with tables and parasols on the front patio, looking out at the rowboats (for hire), the continental illusion is complete, but the stripped pine floor, potted palms, good food and outstanding wine list (150 bins) are ample compensations when the weather is being British. A pianist tickles the ivories four or five nights per week. Owner (since 1989) Clive Pledger is a former chocolatier and patissiere, and a wine connoisseur - he holds occasional wine-tastings. Brasserie may be hired for weddings etc. Easy parking on road.

THE PHEASANT

Keyston, nr Huntingdon. Tel: (01832) 710241, Fax: (01832) 710340

Hours: 12 to 2pm, 6:30 to 10pm daily (bar & restaurant).
Credit cards: Access, Visa, Diners, Amex.
Price guide: a la carte £17.50.

Examples from menus (revised fortnightly): *double-baked goats' cheese soufflé with apple & walnut salad; chicken, mushroom & basil sausage with braised lentils & vegetables; fillet of red mullet cured in honey & spices with spiced tomato & coriander sauce. Roast saddle of venison with red cabbage & celeriac purée; baked fillet of cod with herb crust & thyme sauce; char-grilled vegetables with potato & chive salad & red pepper sauce. Citrus lemon tart with creme fraiche; passion fruit delice; rich chocolate marquis with coffee sauce. Trad. Sun. roasts.*

The Michelin red 'M' is not easily acquired, and is further testimony (to add to high praise in virtually all the major national guides) to the excellence of this picturesque 17th-century thatched inn. A classic of its kind, it is replete with old timbers and log fires, and overlooks a textbook village green, but a glance at the menu above will confirm this is much more a sophisticated restaurant than a country pub (although drinkers are made welcome). It is as relaxed as any pub, however, in keeping with its stablemates, the Three Horseshoes at Madingley, Old Bridge Hotel in Huntingdon and White Hart, Gt Yeldham. Like them it also boasts an outstanding wine list. Chef patron is Martin Lee, who has worked at the celebrated Le Manoir Aux Quat' Saisons and with Paul Heathcote. Functions up to 30 in restaurant.

BENNETT'S RESTAURANT AT THE WHITE HART
Bythorn, nr Huntingdon. Tel: (01832) 710226

Hours: restaurant 12 to 2pm, 7 to 9:30pm except Sun. evenings & Mondays;
bar lunch & evening every day except Sat. evenings.
Credit cards: Access, Visa, Switch.
Price guide: a la carte £20.

Examples from menus (revised 5-weekly): *kipper paté; potted pigeon; green herb terrine. Fillet steak & kidney pudding; salmon & scallop parcels with lobster sauce; crispy pancake stuffed with fresh vegetables & pine kernels with tomato & rosemary sauce; half roast Gressingham duck with honey, soy sauce and ginger. Bar: crispy loin of pork; crispy prawns in batter; game casserole; toasted brie with bacon; sirloin steak; 3-cheese ploughman's; daily specials eg spare ribs, faggots with onions, mussels in white wine. Home-made sorbets; toasted fresh fruit sabayon. Trad. Sun. roasts.*

Opened on the same day that that the old main road by which it stands was by-passed, The White Hart, more a restaurant than a pub (although drinkers are most welcome), hasn't needed passing trade. Just a mile off the new A14 in a peaceful hamlet, it draws custom from many miles around and has also not gone unnoticed by many of the major national food guides. The fact that it was once three cottages is immediately obvious on entering: stripped-wood floors, low ceilings and a truly magnificent open fireplace engender a rare sense of real atmosphere. A photo from 1910, displayed in the conservatory restaurant (which doubles for functions), shows how little things have changed. Cooking, too, is rooted in the best traditions, yet always imaginative. This food orientation extends to the reading matter thoughtfully provided by Bill and Pam Bennett in the bar. They and the cheerful staff infuse the place with a lively personality. Children welcome. Garden.

THE BELL INN HOTEL & RESTAURANT
Great North Road, Stilton. Tel: (01733) 241066, Fax: (01733) 245173

Hours : 12 to 2pm, 7 to 9:30pm daily, bar & restaurant.
Credit cards : Visa, Access, Switch.
Price guide : set price a la carte £22.50 (4 courses), table d'hote £15.95, lunch £13.50
Accommodation : 2 sngls, 14 dbls/twins, 1 family, 2 4-posters, all en suite with TV (incl. SKY), phone, haidryers, ironing boards, tea & coffee, some with whirlpool baths. Singles from £59, doubles/twins from £74. Special weekend breaks.

Examples from menus (revised weekly): *salmon & scallop timbale with tomato & coriander sauce; stilton filo baskets. Escalope of venison filled with chicken & chestnut forcemeat on cream & mushroom sauce garnished with truffle; lamb reforme; panache Cherburg (fresh fish gently steamed, coated with cognac & lobster sauce, with Dublin Bay prawn). Sweets from pastry kitchen; stilton & plum bread. Bar: Normandy soup; cajun prawns; steaks; Bell beef pie; baguettes.*

This is one of England's great (and oldest) historic coaching inns, but now that the old A1 has been by-passed it enjoys the tranquility of a country retreat. The 16th-century stonework and timbers have witnessed many a famous face: Dick Turpin, Cromwell, Lord Byron, Clark Gable and Joe Louis amongst them, not forgetting Cooper Thornhill, an 18th-century landlord who first popularised Stilton as one of the world's noblest cheeses. Modern amenities and comforts have been blended skilfully with ancient character: bedrooms are of a luxury undreamt of by earlier travellers, likewise the first class cuisine, which has won accolades from Egon Ronay and other major guides, and the ACE Hotel of the Year 1995 Award. EATB 4 Crowns Highly commended. Excellent facilities for conferences, meetings, wedding receptions etc.

THE CHERRY HOUSE RESTAURANT

125 Church Street, Werrington Village, Peterboro'. Tel: (01733) 571721

Hours: 12 to 2pm Tues - Fri & Sun; 7 to 10pm Tues - Sat.
Credit cards: Mastercard, Visa, Amex.
Price guide: table d'hote £15.95; lunch £12.50 (2 courses), £15.95 (3 courses).

Examples from menus (revised weekly): *venison & pistachio nut sausage on bed of braised red cabbage, cordoned with redcurrant & port jus; filo pastry basket filled with seafood in light Dijon mustard & dill cream sauce. Duo of grilled brill & salmon fillets on bed of leeks with chive butter sauce; medallions of Grasmere Farm pork fillets served with prune & marsala sauce; vegetable & nut strudel served with stilton & port cream sauce. Rich chocolate mousse (spec.); home-made cheesecakes; poached pears with brandysnaps (fruit straight from garden). Trad. Sun. roasts plus alternatives.*

Being chef as well as proprietor, Andrew Corrick can achieve that elusive consistency which is so important. Fresh produce is another key factor, and you don't get much fresher than fruit straight from the garden. Werrington Village (not to be confused with 'new' Werrington) is an island of antiquity in the modern sprawl of Peterborough, and this 400-year-old thatched cottage is its most picturesque building, inside as well as out. A conservatory is used for private parties and there's room for a marquee in the garden. Only minutes from Peterborough, The Cherry House makes an excellent meeting place and is popular for business lunches. Prices are remarkably modest for a restaurant of this standing - children under 10 eat at half price.

OLD BRIDGE HOTEL

1 High Street, Huntingdon. Tel: (01480) 452681, Fax: (01480) 411017

Hours: 12 to 2:30pm,
6 to 10:30pm daily
(bar & restaurant).
Credit cards: Access, Visa,
Diners, Amex.
Price guide: A la carte £18.
Accommodation: 7 sngls,
19 dbls/twins. All
en suite, satellite
TV, hair dryer,
trouser press,
complimentary
newspaper. Rooms
from £67.50 to
£120 per night.
Special weekend
breaks £67.50
(dinner, b & b).

Examples from menus (revised monthly): *warm potato latkes with smoked salmon & sour cream; thin pastry tart with artichokes, olives, aubergine, mozarella, oregano & pistou; chicken liver parfait with grilled brioche. Pan-fried John Dory with ratatouille and pan-fried pasta; cassoulet of rabbit & duck; fillet of beef with roast potatoes, mange touts, celeriac puree and bacon, mushroom & red wine sauce. Lunchtime buffet Mon - Fri. Sunday lunch: roast sirloin of beef.*

One of the most respected and best known in the county, this elegant 18th-century hotel (the flagship of the Huntsbridge Group of The Pheasant, Keyston, Three Horseshoes, Madingley and White Hart, Gt Yeldham) is also one of the most opulent. Richly decorated throughout with the finest fabrics (and the bathrooms are luxurious!), it remains nonetheless remarkably 'unstarchy'. The staff are cheerful and courteous, and one may eat what and where one likes. Chef patron Nick Steiger is experienced in top establishments in London and Oxford, while Managing Director John Hoskins is the industry's only "Master of Wine" and winner of Egon Ronay's "Cellar of the Year" for the best wine list in the UK (many available by the glass). The restaurant is clearly no mere appendage, and rates in just about every leading national guide. But the hotel is well situated for an overnight stay, on the banks of the River Ouse and just a short stride from the shops. Cambridge and Grafham water are easily reached. Function room for 30. Live jazz on the terrace first Friday of each month.

THE THREE HORSESHOES

Madingley, nr Cambridge. Tel: (01954) 210221, Fax: (01954) 212043

Hours: 12 to 2pm, 6:30 to 10pm daily (bar & restaurant).
Credit cards: Access, Visa, Diners, Amex.
Price guide: a la carte £18.

Examples from menus (revised three-weekly): *chargrilled scallops with wilted raddicio, chard & chicory, with 30-year-old balsamic vinegar & chive oil; Tuscan bread soup with tomato, beans, cabbage & olive oil. Grilled skate wing with butter beans, rosemary, spinach & lemon butter; pan-fried duck with duck confit, champ, green cabbage, bacon & lentils with red wine & thyme; twice-baked aubergine & ricotta soufflé; roast haunch of venison with red onion marmalade, fondant potato, leeks, mushrooms & juniper. Sunday lunch: roast sirloin of beef.*

Cambridge is surely the region's most visited city, and the consequent bustle can be quite taxing. But just two miles away is to be found this idyllic retreat, a 17th-century thatched inn surrounded by parkland. Highly rated by nearly all the major national good food and pub guides, it is best described as a quality restaurant, although guests are most welcome to just call in for a drink in the bar. One may dine in the bar or the elegant conservatory overlooking the large garden. Richard Stokes is the chef patron, having trained at the famous George Hotel, Stamford and Flitwick Manor. Managing Director is John Hoskins, a wine expert of national standing, whose aim is to list the 100 most interesting wines to be found. Egon Ronay and the Italian Wine Trade have judged the choice to be outstanding. The Three Horseshoes flourishes as part of the prestigious quartet which includes the Old Bridge Hotel at Huntingdon, The Pheasant at Keyston and White Hart, Gt Yeldham, and follows the same philosophy of friendly informality.

SHEEN MILL HOTEL & RESTAURANT

Station Road, Melbourn. Tel: (01763) 261393, Fax: (01763) 261376

Hours: 12:30 to 2pm, 7:30 to 10pm. Morning coffees.
Bar meals in conservatory lunchtimes only.
Credit cards: Access, Visa, Diners, Amex.
Price guide: a la carte from £23, special dinner menu £22.50, lunch from £15.95.
Accommodation: 4 doubles (from £75), 4 singles (£50). All en suite, TV,
direct phone, hair dryer, tea & coffee.

Examples from menus (revised seasonally): *ballantine of foie gras with toasted brioche & Gewurtzraminer jelly; grilled scallops on 'lentilles du Puy' and coriander butter; feuillette of asparagus & oyster mushrooms with roasted shallots & light cream sauce. Fillet of beef encased in wild mushroom mousse & savoy cabbage with Madeira sauce; roulade of guinea fowl & spinach with Noilly Prat & saffron sauce; grilled fillet of sea bass with red pepper coulis & deep fried leeks; flambes and vegetarian dishes. Fresh orange mousse served on crisp biscuit with blackberry sauce; warm chestnut & strega pudding with vanilla custard.*

The individually-decorated bedrooms of this charming 17th-century mill all overlook a glorious canvas, and guests can enjoy the riverside setting from the conservatory perched on the water's edge. Proprietors (for 17 years) Jenny and Carlo Cescutti have built a reputation for fine foods and wine in one of East Anglia's most acclaimed establishments. In the elegant peach, cream and grey restaurant (also with fine views), award-winning Head Chef John Curtis (recognised at an early age by Ackerman as among the top 500) prides himself on innovation and insists that all is fresh and home-made - even the delicious chocolates served with coffee. This has not only won him two AA rosettes and a Michelin red 'M' (one of only 56 in the country), but also a place in Michelin and other leading good food guides. Theme evenings (eg Jazz, Thai, Seafood) last Friday of each month; regular wine-tastings on Thurs & Fri evenings.

THE PINK GERANIUM

Station Road, Melbourn. Tel: (01763) 260215, Fax: (01763) 262110

Hours: open for lunch & dinner, Tues. - Sat., plus Sunday lunch.
Credit cards: Access, Visa, Amex.
Price guide: a la carte £35.40. Table d'hote dinner £20 Tues - Fri;
lunch £10 Tues - Fri; Sun lunch £19.
Available for private hire (private parties/weddings/conferences ect).

Examples from menus (revised seasonally): *pot au feu of king scallops with linguine; goat's cheese soufflé with roasted tomatoes; saddle of venison with juniper berries; vegetarian assiette; lobster with gremolata and tarragon velouté.*

The Pink Geranium's stack of food awards increases yearly. It was recently voted 'National Restaurant of the Year' in a prestigious catering association awards ceremony in 1995. Chef/Proprietor Steven Saunders is known to many as BBC TV's Chef on Ready Steady Cook, cooks and fronts the restaurant with his wife Sally at The Pink Geranium. His kitchen team (headed by Paul Murfitt) create exceptional quality food at very reasonable prices (see above). Ensure you book as it's always busy! The Pink Geranium is a pretty 15th-century thatched cottage set in gardens blooming with geraniums. The restaurant also operates an outside catering company, Steven's Cookery School, a chauffeur service and a delicatessen. Altogether a charming, unforgettable culinary experience in one of the country's best.

THE ANCHOR INN

Sutton Gault, Sutton, nr Ely. Tel: (01353) 778537, Fax: (01353) 776180

Hours : 12 to 2pm, 7 to 9pm daily.
Credit cards : Mastercard, Visa, Switch, Delta, Amex.
Price guide : a la carte £22, set-price lunch £14.95 (3 courses),
lunchtime specials from £5.
Accommodation : 2 dbls/twins, both en suite, sitting room, TV, phone, dryer,
tea & coffee. TB 3 Crowns Highly Commended, AA QQQQ.
From £55 per room. Special 3-night winter breaks.

Examples from menus (revised daily): *grilled dates wrapped in bacon on a mild mustard sauce; herring fillets in Madeira marinade. Fresh fillet of salmon with watercress cream; wild rabbit braised in cider with bacon, mustard, prunes & herbs; steak, kidney & Guinness pie; mushroom, herb, red wine & blue cheese pancake. Passion fruit creme brulée with home-made vanilla biscuit; chocolate Bavarian cream with apricot sauce. Good selection of cheeses. Bar (lunchtime only): own-recipe sausages in red wine with garlic mash; wild mushroom omelette; potted duck with crusty bread. Trad. Sun. roasts.*

Les Routiers Inn of the Year; Cambridge Dining Pub of the Year from another major guide; a Rosette from the Consumer's Association; featured on local TV: despite its glorious solitude, this remarkably preserved (the bar is still gaslit) 350-year-old riverside ferry inn is well and truly 'on the map', even if Sutton Gault itself is not (turn off the B1381 in Sutton village). Credit is due to proprietor Robin Moore, assisted by chef Mark Corcoran; their everchanging menus are supplemented by monthly Gourmet Nights on Tuesdays in winter, and there's occasional wine tasting (ask to go on mailing list). Spectacular sunsets and views from bedroom windows. Small function room.

177

THE FEN HOUSE RESTAURANT
2 Lynn Road, Littleport, nr Ely. Tel: (01353) 860645

Hours : 7 to 9pm (last orders), Tues - Sat. Sunday lunch by arrangement.
Credit cards : Access, Visa, Diners.
Price guide : set price a la carte £24.50 (4 courses); lunch by arrangement.

Examples from menus (revised monthly): *puff pastry case filled with shredded skate & watercress with watercress sauce; fillets of smoked haddock with quails' eggs & wild rice. Rack of lamb with garlic fritters & parsley cream; roast saddle of wild rabbit with mustard noodles; excellent vegetarian options. Caramelised roasted pears with honey ice cream; rich chocolate mousse sandwiched between crisp chocolate layers surrounded by raspberry sauce.*

Michelin and other acknowledged arbiters of good taste laud this little 22-seater gem, heartily endorsed by a well established clientele. David and Gaynor Warne have worked hard over nine years to earn this recognition for their comfortable, elegant 17th-century cottage out in the 'wilds' of Fenland. One may arrive by car, boat or train (the river and station are very near), but can always look forward to a warm reception from Gaynor, and a well considered and balanced menu prepared by David himself (formerly of The Savoy and Buckingham Palace), to be savoured in relaxed surroundings. All is fresh and homemade, even bread and ice cream, and many of the vegetables are organically grown. 50 or so wines appear on a very good, reasonably priced list. Ask to go on the waiting list for membership of the LUNCHEON CLUB (£10 fee); it's very friendly, with lively discussion over a three-course meal and wine.

THE ORANGERY RESTAURANT AT CONGHAM HALL

Grimston, near King's Lynn. Tel: (01485) 600250, Fax: (01485) 601191

Hours: 12:30 to 2pm, 7:30 to 9:30pm, daily except Sat. lunchtime.
Credit cards: Access, Visa, Diners, Amex.
Price guide: set price a la carte dinner £25 & £32 incl. coffee. Lunch £15,
light lunches from £3.25.
Accommodation: 14 rooms (all en suite), from £75 single, £99 double.
Weekend breaks from £155pp h/b.

Examples from menus (revised seasonally): *terrine of confit chicken studded with prunes & served with seasonal leaves; ravioli of mixed shellfish with lobster butter sauce. Pot-roast honey-glazed shank of lamb with parmentier potatoes & rosemary & tomato jus; fettucini of salmon, broccoli & sun-dried tomatoes in basil butter sauce; fricassee of local field mushrooms in puff pastry with chive butter sauce. Caramelised creme brulee infused with Bailey's, served with almond biscuit. Trad. Sun. roasts.*

The RAC blue ribbon, AA rosettes and red stars are not casually awarded, but Congham Hall has them all, a rare achievement for proprietors Trevor and Christine Forecast, who supervise personally. Recent accolades are Johansen's 'Hotel of the Year 1993', a 'Cesar' from the Good Hotel Guide for being 'The Epitome of the English Country Hotel', and for 1996 an Egon Ronay Star for chef Jonathan Nicholson. A member of the exclusive 'Pride of Britain' consortium, theirs is surely one of the most prestigious country hotels in the region, a Georgian Manor set in 40 acres of lovely parkland and gardens, including a large kitchen herb garden, open to the public at certain times. Yet for all this, one may enjoy a lunch of chef's fresh, innovative cooking in the stylish new ORANGERY RESTAURANT, speedily served and in "formal informality", at prices comparable to a pub.

RISTORANTE LA VILLETTA

14 High Street, Heacham. Tel: (01485) 570928

Hours: 12 to 2pm (2:30 Suns) Tues - Sat, 7 to 10pm weekdays; 6 to11pm Sats.
Credit cards: Access, Visa.
Price guide: a la carte £16, lunch from £5. Sun lunch set price £8.95 &
£9.95 (2 & 3 courses).

Examples from menu (revised seasonally): *local cockles sauteed in red wine with chives & parsley; vegetable tartlet in tomato sauce; pastas. Fillets of lemon sole poached in white wine with prawn, cucumber & cream sauce; breast of chicken stuffed with paté & wrapped in puff pastry; escalope of veal with peppers, mushrooms, garlic & tomato sauce; vegetable roast. Apple pie; bread & butter pudding; treacle sponge; luxury Italian ice creams. Trad. Sun. roasts with fish alternative & full a la carte.*

Building on early success (the visitors' book is full of enthusiastic remarks), Carl (front of house) and Deborah (chef) Godfrey are ever eager to please and continue to offer exceptional value. If you just fancy a pasta and glass of wine, that's fine, but you will be tempted by an extensive menu and wine list with a distinct Italian flavour, but now including a selection of English and New World wines, again at very fair prices. Guests are encouraged to linger, Italian-style; the newly extended conservatory is an ideal place in which to do so. For something different look out for theme nights, such as Fish, or the quarterly Ladies' Evenings - a chance to socialise and see a demonstration or two. The no-smoking restaurant is cool and elegant, plushly carpeted, pink and blue linen, flowers on each table, whirring ceiling fans. Watercolours by local artists are for sale. Children welcome. Car park to rear.

FISHES' RESTAURANT

Market Place, Burnham Market. Tel: (01328) 738588

Hours: lunch & dinner (last orders 9:30pm, 9pm in winter) Tues - Sun.
Closed over Christmas and two weeks in January.
Credit cards: Access, Visa, Diners, Amex.
Price guide: a la carte £20, weekday lunch £8.95 & £11.25 (2 & 3 courses).

Examples from menus (revised seasonally): *fresh fish terrine; local oysters live or baked with stilton; crab soup; melon & fresh fruit. Monkfish with mussel & orange sauce; salmon fishcakes with crab sauce; turbot fillet with prawn & parsley sauce; crustacean plate; smoked eel; river trout with almonds & bananas; home-baked ham with smoked chicken. Orange & raisin cheesecake; bread & butter pudding; chocolate & Cointreau mousse; bramley, bramble & plum crumble; tiramisu; home-made ice creams; fresh fruit salad. Mostly British cheeses eg Pencarrig. Children's portions.*

Burnham Market is one of Norfolk's most picturesque villages, and indeed historic: Nelson was born and raised very near here - take away the cars and he would still feel at home today. Another link with the North Sea where he learnt his craft is this perennially popular restaurant, which draws on its bounty in the form of oysters from Brancaster, crabs from Weybourne or Blakeney and much else from King's Lynn. Vegetables come fresh from local market gardeners. Featured regularly in a number of leading national good food guides, it remains nonetheless cheerfully unpretentious bistro-style, with cork tables and floors, shelves full of books on a multitude of topics, and in summer windows full of 'Morning Glories.' Live lobsters are kept in a tank out of sight, but the cold display is mouthwatering.

THE CROWN HOTEL

The Buttlands, Wells-next-the-Sea. Tel: (01328) 710209, Fax: (01328) 711432

Hours: 12 to 2pm, 7 to 9:15pm daily.
Credit cards: Access, Visa, Amex, Diners.
Price guide: a la carte from £18, table d'hote £18, a la carte from £7.50), Sun.
lunch £8.50.
Accommodation: 1 single, 10 doubles/twins, 4 family. Bargain breaks.

Examples from menus (revised periodically): *duck pate with truffles; maraschino cherries & brandy; choux pastry gougere with prawns, tomatoes & onions, capped with cheese. Fresh local lobster; pigeon breasts sauteed with bacon, with cream sauce of wild mushrooms; steak & kidney pie; vegetable tagliatelle in tomato & soy sauce. Chef's desserts.*

"The sort of hotel that tired travellers dream about" - so says the Times newspaper. Who knows, perhaps Horatio Nelson scanned the pages of an earlier edition over breakfast here at The Crown, for it was from this Tudor hotel that he departed in 1793 to join his ship "Agamemnon." Latterly it was Sir Peter Scott, famous ornithologist, who took rest and refreshment beneath the venerable exposed timbers, this coast being a Mecca for "twitchers." The beach, a mile out from the harbour and backed by pinewoods, is magnificent, and the town itself is quaint enough to be still recognisable to Lord Nelson. Proprietor Wilfred Foyers is a distinguished practitioner of the culinary arts, and has won many commendations, including the RAC Blue Ribbon award. The everchanging menus are complemented by a carefully considered wine list presented with an explanatory map. Children welcome in certain areas, dogs also. New Garden Room sun lounge.

MORSTON HALL

Morston, nr Blakeney. Tel: (01263) 741041, Fax: (01263) 740419

Hours : 7:30 for 8pm every evening. Sunday lunch.
Credit cards : Access, Visa, Amex.
Price guide : Set dinner £23 (4 courses & coffee), lunch £14 (3 crs).
Accommodation : 6 doubles/twins, all en suite, with TV, direct 'phone, tea & coffee,
hair dryer. From £65 pp dinner, bed & b/fast.
Bargain breaks Nov, Dec, March, April 3 nights £175pp incl
plus afternoon tea on arrival. Tourist Brd Highly Commended.

Examples from menus (changed daily): *vegetable terrine; homemade pasta; roasted red pepper & tomato soup; sole turban with mushroom mousse; wild duck with liver stuffing. Rich chocolate torte; champagne jelly with brandy syllabub.*

"Best Newcomer of the Year 1993" (Caterer & Hotelkeeper); "County Hotel of the Year" in a leading good hotel guide; AA two red stars and rosettes; a much coveted red-letter award from a major French organisation: yet more accolades to add to the many accrued by proprietors Justin Fraser, Galton and Tracy Blackiston since they acquired this 17th-century farmhouse hall in March 1992. Much of their trade is repeat business, which is perhaps the most eloquent testimony of all. Personal service and first class food (Galton is a very experienced chef) are essential ingredients, but the Hall itself is full of charm. Bedrooms are huge and beautifully furnished, and the two lounges and restaurant are spacious and most comfortably appointed. Fruits, vegetables and herbs are grown in the 3-acre garden, and other local produce is also favoured in the kitchen. Unusually, wine is listed according to grape rather than nationality. Look out for special evenings (eg Guy Fawkes). Private parties welcome. Two dog kennels. Residential cookery courses.

WENSUM LODGE HOTEL
Bridge Street, Fakenham. Tel: (01328) 862100, Fax: (01328) 863365

Hours : Mon - Sat 11:30am to 3pm, 6:30pm to 10pm; Sun 12 to 2:30pm,
7 to 9:30pm.
Credit cards : Access, Visa, Diners, Amex, Switch, JCB.
Price guide : a la carte £15; bar snacks from £1.75.
Accommodation : 2 sngls (£40), 7 dbls/twins (£55). All en suite, TV, phone, tea & coffee.
(hair dryer available). Special 3-night breaks £120 sngl, £180 dbl for
dinner, b & b (incl. £10pp dinner allowance + glass of wine).

Examples from menu (revised seasonally): *freshly-dressed local crab garni; melon crown filled with local strawberries. Roast duck breast with redcurrant & brandy sauce; fresh lobster thermidor; oven-baked halibut with lemon & cream sauce; giant vol-au-vent filled with local wild mushrooms in Madeira & cream sauce. Bar: baguettes; jacket potatoes; salads; sandwiches. Deep dish apple pie; summer berries of the day with fresh cream. Children's menu. 4-course Sunday lunch £9.00.*

The crystal-clear River Wensum rushes past the front door, and a little stream gurgles through the rear garden (by the car park) - easy to forget one is in the centre of Fakenham. One is also at the heart of the county, ideally placed to explore, with the prospect of fresh local produce, prepared by chef Glen Bishop and staff in the open-view kitchen, to return to. Value for money is exceptional: Pasta Night on Thursdays, for example, is when you may eat as much as you like for £5.95; Friday is Sizzling Steak Night - £10 for two courses. Sympathetically converted from a grain store of uncertain age, the restaurant (with family no-smoking area) is not short of character, and with such a setting is ideal for a wedding reception (up to 150 guests). In fact, you can now even get married here as well!

THE MIRABELLE

Station Road, West Runton, Cromer. Tel: (01263) 837396

Hours : open for lunch & dinner (last orders 9:15pm). Closed Mondays;
closed Sunday evenings in winter.
Credit cards : Access, Visa, Diners, Amex.
Price guide : a la carte £17.50 - £22.50. Table d'hote £15 - £23.50.
Lunch £10.50 - £12.95.
Accommodation : self-contained flat (sleeps 2) from £50 per week in winter to £175
in summer; special all-inclusive breaks.

Examples from menus (a la carte revised seasonally, table d'hote daily): *local asparagus; Cromer crab; Hungarian goulash soup; seafood vol-au-vent; mussels. Salmon & sea bass in butter sauce; turbot; Dover sole; lobster mayonnaise/thermidor; calves liver & sweetbreads; Wienerschnitzel; game in season. Creme brulee; Viennoise apple strudel; fresh figs in Marsala; souffle glace Grand Marnier.*

A newcomer would never anticipate that behind such an outwardly modest facade lies a large, bustling French restaurant, or that the proprietor, Manfred Hollwoger, is Austrian - hence the Germanic flavour to some of the dishes. Two set price menus and an a la carte add up to en extensive choice, with local seafood and game the house specialities, and vegetarians not forgotten. Even the most conventional dish is cooked and presented in a way that makes it memorable. Portions are very generous; you will not go away disappointed! A truly splendid wine list of over 350 is one of the largest in the country. Gourmet nights in winter should not be missed - ask for a schedule. Do try to book ahead in summer and for weekends at any time, for this is one of the most popular restaurants in the area. Now in its 23rd year, The Mirabelle is a perennial in national good food guides, and a North-Norfolk institution. Well appointed accommodation is an extra bonus.

THE PEPPERPOT VILLAGE RESTAURANT
Water Lane, West Runton, nr Sheringham. Tel: (01263) 837578

Hours: 12 - 2pm Tues to Sun, 7 - 10pm Tues to Sat.
Credit cards: Visa, Mastercard, Eurocard, Amex, Diners Club International.
Price guide: a la carte from £18, table d'hote £16.95, set price 3-course lunch £10.50.
Sunday lunch £10.95.

Examples from menus (revised 3-4 months): *grilled mussels in garlic sauce; melting pots of salmon & prawns; mushrooms in stilton cheese sauce. Dover sole; baked sea bass with fennel; lobster thermidor; swordfish; tournedos chasseur; venison in port & redcurrant sauce; daily home-made vegetarian dish. Lemon soufflé; cygnet surprise (meringue swan filled with fresh fruit & cream with raspberry coulis & ice cream). Choice of three Sunday roasts & supreme of salmon in white butter sauce.*

Royalty and other dignitaries have enjoyed the cooking of Ron Gattlin; during his 34 years with the RAF he was chef to Chief of Air Staff and in charge of catering at RAF training college, Bracknell. Now we humble civilians can also partake, here at his own beamed and chintzy restaurant quietly situated just off the main coast road, where he and wife Barbara (front of house) have earned a place in local esteem over the past five years or so. With such depth of experience his 'repertoire' is truly comprehensive, but he does show a special flair for fresh vegetables, always interestingly presented, and for diet-busting cakes and pastries. Yet prices remain modest, even by the standards of this parsimonius region! Romantics should note in their diaries that Valentine's Supper, five courses plus nibbles to start and coffee with mints to finish, is all for just £21.50 currently, and no extra for the candlelight and flowers on each table!

LLOYD'S RESTAURANT
66 London Street, Norwich. Tel: (01603) 624978, Fax: (01603) 767382

Hours : 12 to 2pm Mon - Sat, 6:45pm to 9:30pm Tues - Sat.
Credit cards : Access, Visa, Diners, Amex.
Price guide : a la carte £17, lunch & early evening set price £10 (3 courses).

Examples from menus (revised seasonally): *salmon fishcakes pan-fried with tartare sauce; country pork & herb terrine with home-made chutney; freshly-cooked tagliatelle with tomato & fresh basil sauce. Poached fillet of brill with light Dijon mustard & cream sauce; local wild rabbit braised in dark ale, rosemary & cider sauce; home-made herb sausages. Victoria plum pavlova; hot chocolate souffle; tarte citrone; fruit crumble.*

Modern British cooking is very much in vogue but is perhaps best enjoyed continental-style: there are tables with parasols on the pedestrianised street outside, one of the city's most attractive. If weather does not permit, the first-floor 18th-century restaurant has its compensations: wood-panelled, its mostly benched seating is arranged in 'compartments', affording intimacy, and together with felicitous use of drapes and old photos, the effect is homely without being twee. Since opening in 1982, Lloyd and Cynthia Addison (both chefs) have established themselves as leading exponents of their art, and continue to offer amazingly good value, with a resultant loyal following. Yet all is freshly prepared on the premises, including the bread. Those who also seek mental stimulation should not miss the regular historical supper slide shows or tutored wine evenings. The international wine list numbers some good desserts and many half-bottles.

ADLARD'S

79 Upper St. Giles Street, Norwich. Tel: (01603) 633522

Hours : 12:30 to 1:45pm, Tues. - Sat. 7:30 to 10:30pm, Mon. - Sat.
Credit cards : Access, Visa, Amex.
Price guide : set price £31 (3 courses), £34 (4 courses). Priced by the course.
Lunch £13.50 (2 courses), £16.50 (3 courses).

Examples from menus (revised daily): *seized turbot with gratin of Mediterranean vegetables and basil tomato vinaigrette; grilled teal with salsa verde, pinenuts & herb salad; puff pillow of locally picked wild mushrooms with Madeira sauce. Skate with grain mustard butter sauce & fresh tagliatelle; loin of venison with spatzle, bacon & quenelle of horseradish cream & gratin dauphinois; rack of English lamb with tapenade crust, tart of onion confit & glazed baby onions. Mille feuilles of white chocolate & caramelised bananas; summer pudding with lime syllabub.*

"County Restaurant of the Year" in a leading national good food guide, and recipient of a Michelin Star, this is one of the region's élite, with a reputation which extends far beyond. David and Mary Adlard moved about eight years ago to this 18th-century grade II listed building in a bustling cul-de-sac near the R.C. Cathedral. David learned his craft at The Connaught, London, is known as a determined perfectionist, and has appeared on national TV, but for all the formidable reputation there is no pretentiousness: simple polished beech flooring on three tiers is complemented by striking green wall fabric and original oil paintings, and the atmosphere is relaxed and unstarchy. Prices are also well within reach, and indeed the lunch menus offer very good value for a restaurant of this calibre. Exceptional wine list of 250 bins from all over the world.

BRASTED'S

8-10 St. Andrews Hill, Norwich, Tel: (01603) 625949, Fax: (01603) 766445

Hours: Mon. - Fri. 12 to 2pm and 7 to 10pm. Sat. 7 to 10pm.
Credit cards: Access, Visa, Diners, Amex.
Price guide: a la carte £24. Club Lunch £8.50, £12.50 & £16 (2,3 & 4 courses).

Examples from menus (revised seasonally): *tart of smoked haddock & leek with watercress sauce; Brasted's filo pastry cheese parcels with homemade apple & thyme jelly; quenelles of salmon in lobster sauce. Lowestoft brill in cream, mushroom & prawn sauce; braised lamb shanks with lentils; breasts of wild duck with Madeira & green peppercorn sauce; casserole of vegetables. Chocolate Marquise on coffee bean sauce (irresistible!); baked apple with apricots, sultanas & almonds on warm rum-scented apricot sauce; hot souffles. Savoury alternatives (a rare treat).*

John Brasted's philosophy, that one should be able to enjoy fine wines at a manageable cost, is born out by the excellent wine list, very keenly priced for a restaurant of such high standing. The same may be said of the cooking: the Club Lunch represents outstanding value - why not make the most of it while shopping or exploring the interesting streets and alleys here in the historic city centre, by the ancient Bridewell Prison, now a museum. First take drinks in the homely morning room, then into the dining room. The welcoming, comfortable atmosphere is enhanced by draped walls and luxurious armchairs on a polished wood floor with Persian rugs, coupled with first-class service free of undue servility. Dishes featured constantly on a new, more extensive menu include tart of fresh tomatoes, the filo pastry cheese parcels (above), quenelles of salmon in rich lobster sauce, and two specialities: a wonderul cassoulet and beef Stroganoff. Maximum use of fresh local produce is evident, sympathetically treated by chef Adrian Clarke.

189

NUMBER 24

24 Middleton Street, Wymondham. Tel: (01953) 607750

Hours: lunch Tues - Sat., dinner from Wed - Sat.
Credit cards: Access, Visa.
Price guide: set price dinner £16.95, lunch £10 (3 courses).

Examples from menus (revised fortnightly): *oxtail & tomato broth with horseradish dumplings; lime-cured salmon; smoked cod & spring onion cakes. Pigeon with beetroot & sour cream mash; spiced chicken with pickled vegetables, root ginger & soy; roasted sea bass with creamed leek & black pepper. Bramley apple spice cake & apple sorbet; poached peaches & marzipan ice cream; banana sponge pudding with hot fudge sauce.*

Opened in the summer of '91, this small, popular restaurant goes from strength to strength, receiving much local acclaim from TV, radio and press. The latest accolade, a 'Catey' for the Menu of the Year (equivalent to the film industry's 'Oscar') has been won previously by the likes of the Roux brothers, The Savoy and Dorchester. Add to this an AA Rosette, superb reviews from Egon Ronay and a clutch of impressive press cuttings, and one can see why many of the regulars want to keep No. 24 a secret! But the style of food is not reflected in the price: choosing from six starters, six main courses and a host of sumptuous desserts, the three-course dinner is just £16.95. Free of charge is the famous homemade bread, canapes on arrival and the special atmosphere that is the hallmark of a family-run business. Chef patron Richard Hughes and wife Sue also offer an outside catering service, cookery demonstrations, wine tastings and vegetarian menus - ask to go on the mailing list.

WEAVERS WINE BAR & EATING HOUSE
Market Hill, Diss. Tel: (01379) 642411

Hours : Tues - Fri 12 to 2pm, Mon - Sat 7 to 9:30pm. Not Christmas.
Credit cards : Access, Visa.
Price guide : a la carte £17, table d'hote £12 (3 courses), lunch £7.95 &
£10.75 (2 & 3 courses).

Examples from menus (revised weekly): *salad of thinly sliced oak-smoked fillet of beef with soured cream & chive dressing; pieces of monkfish tossed with roasted pimento, tomato & olives, served on fresh pasta & topped with mascarpone. Roasted rack of English lamb on orange, mint & redcurrant jus lie; steamed fresh salmon set over a bed of spring onions & beansprouts, with lemon & ginger glaze. Baked treacle & ginger sponge with toffee sauce & custard; brown bread ice cream in brandy snap basket.*

The prosperous Weavers' Guild built this as a chapel in the 15th century. The atmosphere today is much more relaxed and convivial, and sustenance is of a less spiritual, more temporal kind: apart from an excellent range of malt whiskies and wines, fresh, reasonably priced food, flavoured by herbs grown in the garden, is always interesting and unusual, whether for lunch or dinner. Thus has a first rate reputation been established by chef proprietor William Bavin and wife Wilma since they opened in April '87, after having restored the building. From the simple wooden tables, each with a vase of flowers, one can ruminate on the passing street life of this pleasant little town, viewed through large windows.

191

THE DOVE RESTAURANT

Wortwell, Harleston (on A143 by-pass). Tel: (01986) 788315

Hours: anytime, but booking required.
Credit cards: Access, Visa.
Price guide: a la carte £15 to £25, Sun. lunch £8.50
Accommodation: 3 doubles/twins (2 en suite), £32 dble, £17.50 sngle, B & B.
Tourist Board 2 Crowns Approved.

Examples from menus (revised seasonally): *seafood pancake; melon with curried prawns. Own-recipe venison pie; ragout fruits de mer; scampi Provencal; coquilles St. Jacques; chicken supreme; own-recipe steak & kidney pie; trout; steaks. Crepe maison (pancake filled with raspberries, or orange or lemon, and pastry cream); meringue Chantilly; syllabub; chocolate eclair.*

Simple country restaurants serving honest home cooked food are among the best reasons for visiting France. However, one need only travel as far as the A143 by-pass near Wortwell (not the village itself) to experience the same pleasure. Chef Patron John Oberhoffer, recipient of the Cordon Culinaire award and the Association Culinaire Francais de Londres winner's medal, is a distinguished practioner of the art of French country cooking. With wife Pat he has over the last 17 years established the Dove as a much admired restaurant, not just for good food but for the unpretentious manner in which it is presented, and at very reasonable prices. The balanced wine list is mostly French, with some German, although special requests are catered for. They are also pleased to cater for private parties up to 30, and offer a good breakfast after a comfortable night in one of the refurbished bedrooms - you are well placed here in the lovely Waveney Valley for business or pleasure. A 'Dove' has stood on this acre of ground, bordering a stream, since around the time of the French Revolution.

QUIGGINS RESTAURANT
2 High Street, Wrentham. Tel: (01502) 675397

Hours: 11:30am to 2pm, 7 to 10pm, except Sunday evenings & Mondays.
Credit cards: Visa, Eurocard, Mastercard, Amex, Switch, JCB.
Price guide: a la carte £14 - £24, Fixed price dinner menu £19. Lunch £9.95 &
£11.95 (2 & 3 courses plus coffee). Sunday lunch £12.50.
Accommodation: Quiggins Cottage (sleeps 2-4), self-catering or with meals taken
at restaurant.

Examples from menus (revised 3 or 4 times per year): *chicken & water chestnut tartlets; Caribbean prawn cocktail. Quigloins (beef sirloin roasted to order - speciality for 2; 24 hrs notice); sole américaine; prawn creole (for 2); chateaubriand (for 2); rognons saute turbigo; Brigit's plum duck; chestnut roast. Traditional German cheesecake; chocolate terrine; praline parfait.*

One of Britain's most easterly restaurants, this former grocer's shop stands on the A12 just two miles from the Heritage Coast. Tastefully converted in 1970, the cosy listed building retains many of its 18th-century features, as well as a particularly ornate cash register. Prices are remarkably modest (and include lemon sorbet and unlimited coffee with chocolates) - no nasty shocks to spoil a relaxed lunch or dinner. Indeed, unhurried informality is the watchword. Members of the BTA Customers Charter, proprietors (since March '90) Jill and Dudley McNally present appetising menus compiled only from the freshest of ingredients. Local and Old English dishes vie with international and modern, and a reputation for fresh fish has been acquired. The wine list reflects this diversity, New World wines being very well represented. The restaurant is one of only two in Suffolk to receive both the 1995 Les Routiers Casserole Award for outstanding cuisine and its Corps d'Elite for excellent wine selection. Dining in garden in summer. Private parties and disabled welcome.

193

THE CRICKETERS

Wangford Road, Reydon, nr Southwold. Tel: (01502) 723603, Fax: (01502) 722194

Hours : 12 to 2pm, 7 to 9pm daily.
Credit cards : Access, Visa, Amex.
Price guide : set price £13.50 (3 courses). Bar snacks & meals from £2.
Accommodation : 9 bedrooms.

Examples from menus (revised daily): *home-made cream of asparagus soup; seafood & pasta salad. Poached halibut steak with mushroom & tarragon sauce; roast baby guinea fowl with Madeira sauce; escalope of pork fillet Sicilian; sauteed lambs' kidneys & mushrooms in red wine sauce. Bar: king prawns in filo pastry with dill mayonnaise; vegetables & pasta baked in creamy cheese sauce topped with toasted almonds; fresh fish; cold meats platter; daily specials. Homemade sweets. Trad. Sun. roasts.*

The Cricketers (formerly The Randolph) has been a centre of rest and recreation since 1892. Recent renovation has clearly enhanced the public rooms, and cricket memorabilia - prints, photographs of local teams, signed bats - adorn the bright yellow walls. The bar and dining room have also been successfully renovated, and above are nine comfortable bedrooms and a light, airy drawing room. Over the past seven years or so Teresa (manageress) and Kevin (chef) Ellis have earned a firm 'thumbs up' from local clientele, reflected in an ever increasing volume of business, drawn back by delicious homecooked food accompanied by the award-winning Adnams ales and wines. Yet more improvements are in the pipeline. Parties of up to 60 can be accommodated in the hotel, many more in marquees on the vast lawn.

THE CROWN HOTEL

High Street, Southwold. Tel: (01502) 722275, Fax: (01502) 727263

Hours: 12:30 to 1:30pm, 7:30 to 9:30pm, 7 days.
Credit cards: Access, Visa, Amex.
Price guide: set price £19.75. Lunch £14.75. Bar meals from £1.95 - £12.50.
Accommodation: 2 singles (£40), 8 doubles/twins (£61), 1 family (£85),
all with private facilities.

Examples from restaurant menus (changed daily): *oak-smoked salmon with quails' eggs & lemon butter sauce; baby spinach salad with melted goats' cheese & roasted pine nuts; Thai soup with coconut milk & Chinese egg noodles. Fillet of sea-reared trout filled with smoked haddock mousse; grilled magret of Suffolk duck with spiced lentils, ginger & carrot sauce; provencal pepper & black olive flan with tomato & feta salad. Orange tart with thin dark chocolate sauce; pistachio & almond filo purses; roast plums with fruit syrup & cream cheese topped with toasted almonds.*

Feted regularly by national newspapers and major food guides, The Crown enjoys a celebrity well beyond the region. Managed by Anne Simpson, it is a flagship for owners Adnams, whose brewery is near, and whose award-winning range of ales is available in both bars. Being also an esteemed wine merchant, the wine list is of course exceptional, with nearly 300 vintages, many available by the glass. But it is as much the food which wins the plaudits. Its popularity means that booking in the restaurant is always advisable. The essence of an 18th-century coaching inn is still much in evidence - antique furniture, old paintings and carved fireplaces - and the individual bedrooms are simple but attractive. Hotel closed one week in January. Limited parking at rear.

THE SWAN HOTEL
Market Place, Southwold. Tel: (01502) 722186, Fax: (01502) 724800

Hours : 12:15 to 1:45pm, 7:00 to 9:30pm, 7 days. Bar meals 12 to 2:30pm
(3pm Sats), 7 days. From late Oct. to Easter restaurant open for
lunch on Sat. & Sun. only.
Credit cards : Access, Visa, Diners, Amex, Switch.
Price guide : 3 daily set dinner menus: £19.95, £26.50, £29.95.
Lunch £11.95 (2 courses), £14.95 (3 courses).
Accommodation : 6 singles (from £46), 37 doubles/twins (from £83), 2 suites from £139).
Midweek winter breaks from £53.50 pp incl. 3-course dinner with coffee.

Examples from menus (changed daily): *two-pepper bavarois surrounded by dill sauce; smoked Loch Fyne salmon stuffed with smoked fish served with a horseradish cream; chicken liver & prune pate on bed of leaves with Cumberland sauce. Roast local partridge served with a puree of celeriac with rich game jus; fillet of cod glazed with mozarella, served on plum tomato dressed with yellow pepper vinaigrette; rump of lamb simply baked & garnished with polenta, served with black olive, garlic & tomato concasse port sauce. Bread & butter pudding glazed with an orange preserve, served warm with fresh cream; Amaretto & cinnamon cream surrounded by vanilla sauce; mille feuille of sable biscuits layered with cream & fresh raspberries.*

Southwold is one of England's last unspoilt coastal towns, an enchanting throw-back to an age long past. At its heart is this classic 17th-century hotel, remodelled in the 1820's, and the period refinement and elegance has not been lost to more recent modernisations. Like all the public rooms, the dining room is beautifully furnished, and serves as well for a function as a private dinner for two. The smaller informal Trellis Room, overlooking a tiny courtyard, is used as an extension or for private parties. Three fixed price menus offer a very considerable choice ranging from English classics to some highly original eclectic suggestions from chef Chris Coubrough. He very much favours fresh seasonal produce, using home grown herbs and own-baked bread. Simpler but still excellent fare is available in the bar, accompanied by an award winning Adnams ale, or perhaps a wine from the celebrated Adnams range - Wine Merchants of the Year in 1992,1993 and 1995. Afternoon teas are another timeless tradition well observed. Bedrooms are very well appointed, individually decorated, and have colour televisions, direct telephones and hair-dryers. Whilst every latest facility is there, the management (led by Carole Wilkin) takes pride in the fact that the hotel continues to provide the very best in ambience, friendly courteous service and first class products. Widely acclaimed in the national press and magazines, this hotel not only serves the needs of one looking for a restful haven of peace, but also the tired business person seeking to relax from a stressful day, or hold an informal business meeting without the interruptions of modern office technology and continous noise of traffic.

THE DUTCH BARN RESTAURANT
Ferry Road, Southwold. Tel: (01502) 723172

Hours: 11am (12pm Sundays) to 2pm, 7 to 10pm every day except Monday.
Credit cards: Access, Visa.
Price guide: a la carte £6.95 - £12.50, table d'hote £9.95 & £12.70
(2 & 3 courses plus coffee).

Examples from menus (revised monthly): *locally-caught seafood & game; avocado baked with prawns & ham. Cod & prawn mornay; trout baked in wine & herbs; home-made steak & kidney pie; beef cooked in beer with herb dumplings; salmon with hollandaise sauce; fillet steak with cream mushroom & brandy sauce; chicken cooked with tarragon cream sauce; duck with plum & ginger glaze; vegetable pasta bake; spinach & mushroom pancakes; daily specials. Exotic ice creams; homemade desserts. Booking advised.*

This 150-year-old fisherman's barn is just 10 mins' pleasant walk (across the famous green of Constitution Hill and along Ferry Road to the harbour) from the centre of Southwold, just yards from the sand dunes and marshes. Since 1984 Mary Colloby (the chef) and husband Winston (front of house) have been serving traditional English and French cuisine - absolutely fresh, of course - very informally and at extraordinarily reasonable prices. All is home-made (even bread rolls and the fudge served with coffee); vegetables are locally grown and fish come from nearby Lowestoft. Before dining have a drink in the cottagey bar (take a look at the intricately carved bar itself). Special occasions like Valentine's Night and Mothering Sunday are observed, and every Saturday evening there's the soft accompaniment of a grand piano and a small dance floor for those who dare. Extensive wine list available by the glass. Water colours by local artists for sale. Children welcome.

THE ANCHOR HOTEL

Walberswick. Tel: (01502) 722112, Fax: (01502) 722283

Hours: 12 to 2pm, 6:30 to 9pm daily.
Credit cards: Access, Visa, Amex, Switch.
Price guide: set dinner £15.75 & £17.75 (3 & 4 courses): bar meals from £2.50.
Accommodation: 2 sngls, 11 dbl/twins. All en suite, TV's, phone, tea & coffee.
From £46.50 per room.

Examples from menus (revised daily): *grilled wood pigeon with apricots & ginger; salad of oriental spiced vegetables. Steamed salmon with fettucini & tomato; pan-fried chicken with Malay spiced lentils; baked cod with cheese & bacon crust. Bar: pan-fried beef with caramelised onions; poached pasta with smoked chicken; Sole Bay fish stew; toasted muffin topped with scrambled egg & bacon. Homemade desserts. Trad. Sun. roasts.*

On the Heritage Coast (Mecca to many artists, ramblers and ornithologists), Walberswick is a delightful throwback to an earlier, less frantic age. The Anchor makes a perfect base from which to explore the locality, which includes Minsmere Nature Reserve, world-famous Snape Maltings and Southwold. Bright, spacious garden rooms (suitable for the disabled) and five further rooms of varying size in the main hotel provide comfortable accommodation for those seeking peace and quiet. Good food and award-winning beers and wines are the hallmark of Adnams' Hotels. Residents' lounge. Children welcome. Easy access to the beach from the hotel grounds.

THE RIVERSIDE RESTAURANT

Quayside, Woodbridge. Tel: (01394) 382587, Fax: (01394) 382656

Hours: lunch 12 to 3pm, Dinner 6 to 10:30pm, daily except Sun. evenings.
Credit cards: Access, Visa, Amex.
Price guide: a la carte £15 - £20, dinner & film package £18. Light lunch from £3.95.

Examples from a la carte (revised seasonally): *tiger prawns pan-fried with tomato & basil pistou; special platter for two - generous selection of hot & cold hors d'oeuvres; smoked trout mousse with pearls of salmon keta. Pan-fried skate wing with capers & shredded parsley; medley of fish & shellfish with vermouth & saffron. Celebrated home-made puddings eg hot toffee pudding with cream or ice cream; terrine of three chocolates with noisette sauce; pancake parcel filled with curacao souffle or rich double chocolate & praline mouss*e.

The Riverside is part of a unique complex containing the luxurious 288-seater theatre/cinema, one of the leading independents in the country. It is thus able to offer a special three-course dinner and film package for only £18, plus the exciting a la carte. The airy garden-style restaurant, flooded with light by day, becomes magical at night by candlelight. Enjoy pre-film/theatre drinks in the atmospheric bar, with its antique theatrical mirror and array of old filmstar photographs, while you choose from the Dinner & Film menu, eating before or after the film of your choice. The friendly staff and culinary skills of Tim Franklin (head chef) and Kevin Franklin also make for a night to remember. In summer stroll by the Riverside and discover the delights of the ornate gazebo: ice cream, French crepes, cappuccino or espresso coffee, to enjoy under the continental-style canopy. Whatever your choice, you will find proprietor Stuart Saunders true to his word: "The best is not always the most expensive."

THE CAPTAIN'S TABLE SEAFOOD RESTAURANT

3 Quay Street, Woodbridge. Tel: (01394) 383145

Hours: lunch & dinner Tues - Sat. 'Bar' meals lunchtime and midweek evenings.
Closed Sundays & Mondays.
Credit cards: Access, Visa, Diners, Amex, Switch.
Price guide: a la carte £16.50, table d'hote £12.95 (3 courses) snacks from £3.25.

Examples from menus (revised frequently): *profiteroles filled with smoked seafood with coriander sauce; terrine of avocado & smoked turkey; local oysters. Coquillage of local fish & shellfish in cheese & sherry sauce; lemon sole fillets filled with prawns in a seafood & ginger sauce; baked aubergine (filled with courgettes, cashew nuts, tomato & basil topped with cheese); sirloin steak. Grand Marnier choc pot; treacle tart with cream; homemade ice creams. Bar meals and daily blackboard specials.*

"According to wind and tide, fisherman's fancy, farmer's whim and gardener's back" - the caveat on the menu (supplemented by a blackboard) is a clue to the fresh provenance upon which diners have been able to rely for nearly 30 years. That's how long Tony Prentice has been running his ever-popular restaurant in one of the region's most attractive and interesting small towns. Yachtsman will often make their way from the quayside straight to The Captains's Table for further communion with the sea and its bounty, although landlubbers are equally keen. The maritime atmosphere is contrived by the felicitous use of fishing nets, seascapes and nautical oddities, including an old diving helmet. The wine list is large and of seriously high quality (not overpriced). If seafood is not your first choice, the vegetarian and meat alternatives are much more than mere afterthought.

KWOK'S RENDEZVOUS

23 St. Nicholas Street, Ipswich. Tel: (01473) 256833

Hours: lunch Mon - Fri (Sat by arrangement), dinner Mon - Sat;
closed Bank Hols.
Credit cards: Access, Visa, Amex.
Price guide: a la carte from £16, set menu from £15.

Examples from menus: *Szechuen sliced pork (on bed of pickled salad with chilli & garlic sauce); sweet & sour wan-tun; prawn with sesame. Five willows sole (crisp fried in sweet & sour sauce); aromatic & crispy duck; Peking beef fillet (sauteed with fruity bean sauce); quick fried lamb with spring onion; chicken in black bean sauce; lotus root sauteed with hot bean paste.*

Listed among the top 20 Chinese restaurants in the U.K. by The Sunday Express, in the top 10 by American Express, in a major good food guide since 1984 and winner of an AA Rosette, clearly this is no run-of-the-mill establishment, and it enjoys the respect of restaurateurs of all kinds in the area. Most important, the public loves it and have been flocking here for over 15 years. That's how long Thomas Kwok has been presenting his mainly Peking, plus Szechuen and Hunan dishes, recognised as the elite of Chinese cooking. The young waiters are smart and mostly English (no ranguage probrem!). Also untypical is the decor, subdued and tasteful, as one would expect of a first rate restaurant. A bit tricky to find (opp. Cromwell Square), but near the town centre and a car park, and well worth seeking out.

THE OLD COUNTING HOUSE RESTAURANT
Haughley, nr. Stowmarket IP14 3NR Tel & Fax: (01449) 673617

Hours : from 12 noon Mon - Fri. and from 7:15pm Mon - Sat.
Credit cards : Access, Visa, Diners, Amex.
Price guide : table d'hote lunch £11.75 & £13 (2 & 3 courses & coffee.) Dinner £20.50
(4 courses & coffee.) Bistro menu starters from £2.60,
main courses from £6.50.

Examples from menus (revised 3-weekly): *mushrooms in vermouth; thinly sliced breast of duck with cherry & cinnamon dressing. Salmon in a paper parcel, with white wine & julienne of vegetables; pork fillet with hazelnut stuffing, with apple & wine sauce; pepper & pine nut slice. Toffee apple tart; creme brulée; chocolate & rum ganache; crostini (French bread topped with cheese, chives, tomato & anchovy).*

Once a bank (hence the name), the long and chequered history of this marvellous old building goes back to the 13th century, the original still intact. Custodians for many years have been Paul and Susan Woods. Susan cooks, and of course all is absolutely fresh. The set price menu is exceptionally good value for four courses and coffee, and there are six choices of starter and main course, plus a selection of home-made sweets. Occasional theme evenings - French, for example - are extremely popular (details on request). The list of over 40 wines includes some excellent examples from Australia and New Zealand. This historic village (once a Roman settlement) is profuse with flowers in season, being winner of Anglia in Bloom for the last four years. It is also distinguished by its medieval street, the finest Motte & Bailey in the region, and a church with only five bells (not the usual six) and leather fire buckets still hanging in the tower. Les Routiers and AA recommended. Easy parking.

For recipe see page 20

SCUTCHERS BISTRO

Westgate Street, Long Melford. Tel: (01787) 310200

Hours: 12 to 2pm, 7 to 9:30pm Tues. - Sat.
Credit cards: Access, Visa, Amex, Switch.
Price guide: a la carte £17.

Examples from menu (revised monthly): *deep-fried fritter of brie on seasonal leaves with raspberry dressing; hot & sour pickled tiger prawn with olive oil & chillis. Roasted fillet of halibut topped with crab & coriander crust on lime dressing; roast breast of chicken on buttered spinach with light curry & prawn sauce; polenta, artichokes & oyster mushrooms with tomatoes & herbs, topped with mozarella. Steamed apricot pudding with apricot sauce & creme fraiche; warm chocolate fudge cake with pecan sauce. Blackboard specials from daily market.*

Twice featured on regional television, lauded annually by the main national guides, Nicholas and Diane Barrett continue to maintain exemplary standards, but in an informal 'bistro' style of cooking and presentation, and at very modest prices. Over 100 wines are listed from all over the world, starting from just £7.90 for house wine, the most expensive being only £26. But before they opened they completely gutted this former pub (The Scutcher's Arms), careful not to lose touch with its ancient origins. Split-level tiled floors, farmhouse furniture, pretty floral wall coverings and curtains, inglenook fireplace and a forest of oak beams make for a refreshingly light and pleasant environment. Equally important, the washrooms are unashamedly luxurious!

THE OLD HOOPS

15 King Street, Saffron Walden. Tel: (01799) 522813

Hours : 12 to 2:15pm, 7 to 10pm, Tues. - Sat.
Credit cards : Access, Visa, Diners, Amex.
Price guide : a la carte dinner £20 - 25, lunch £10 - £15. Set dinner (Tues - Fri only) £11.95 & £12.95, lunch (all week) £6.95 & £7.95 respectively for 2 & 3 courses plus coffee.

Examples from menus (revised frequently): *sopocka (cured loin of pork) with hedgerow bramble jelly; quails' eggs on bed of salad with avocado sauce; musselcress soup. Roasted veal chop with sauce of wild mushrooms, cream & mint; breast of chicken stuffed with apricots on port wine sauce; grilled halibut steak with sauce of capers, herbs & cream; pasta filled with ricotta cheese & mushrooms. Cream-filled hot profiteroles with chocolate sauce; lemon posset.*

Saffron is the world's most expensive spice, and this pleasant little town was once the centre of trade. Also highly valued but far from expensive, 'The Hoops' can be found right in the middle of the main street, and being on the first floor one can reflect on passing street life whilst digesting the best of fresh food prepared to order. Dating from the 14th century and once a pub, informality still prevails - chef patron Ray Morrison prefers it that way, even though he worked in top West End clubs. With his own style of cooking and attention to detail, he and his family have built an excellent reputation over a number of years, earning a regular spot in national guides. There's no minimum spend, and the wine list is modestly priced. Booking advisable at weekends.

THE WHITE HART

Gt Yeldham, nr Halstead. Tel: (01787) 237250. Fax: (01787) 238044

Hours: 12 to 2pm, 6:30 to 9:45pm, daily.
Credit cards: Access, Visa, Diners, Amex, Switch.
Price guide: a la carte £18.

Examples from menus (revised weekly): *courgette & fennel soup; Thai mussels with lemon grass, coriander & green chillies; duck confit terrine with haricot bean puree & pickled beetroot. Steamed fillet of brill with roasted red peppers, potato & chive salad & pesto sauce; tenderloin of pork with red cabbage & apple & Calvados sauce; tagliatelle with pesto sauce, parmesan cheese & tomato & red onion salad. Rich chestnut terrine with chocolate sauce; blackberry & apple crumble with creme fraiche; creme caramel with prunes poached in liqueur muscat. Trad. Sun. roasts.*

Long admired as one of East Anglia's finest Tudor houses, The White Hart is now also marked as amongst its leading restaurants, having recently been acquired by the Huntsbridge Group (Old Bridge, Huntingdon; Pheasant, Keyston; Three Horseshoes, Madingley). Apart from high standards, there's no group 'formula': chef patron Roger Jones has free rein to develop a distinctive style, augmented by regional theme evenings (eg Tuscany, Piedmont). A common feature, though, is an outstanding wine list. One may dine in bar and restaurant; the atmosphere throughout is very special. Small functions and wedding receptions catered for. Large garden.

THE OLD MOOT HOUSE RESTAURANT

1 St James Street, Castle Hedingham. Tel & Fax: (01787) 460342

Hours : 12 to 2pm Tues - Sun (not Sats); 7 to 9:30pm Tues - Thurs,
7 to 10pm Fri & Sat.
Credit cards : Access, Visa, Diners, Switch, Delta.
Price guide : a la carte £16-23, table d'hote midweek special menu from £13,
lunch from £10 (2 courses incl. wine), plus inexpensive light
snacks & lunches.

Examples from menus (revised regularly, plus weekly specials): *calves liver avocado; king prawns wrapped in filo pastry with oriental spicy mayonnaise; smoked duck breast with homemade cranberry & port sauce. Fillet of red snapper with orange, brandy & cream sauce, garnished with scallops; fillet steak Rossini; chicken en croute with pesto & garlic sauce. Strawberry & kiwi meringue roulade; triple chocolate cake; bread & butter pudding; home-made ice creams. Traditional Sunday roasts + alternatives.*

Lunch, Light Lunch & Evening Specials menus also available.

Michael and Maureen Medcraft welcome guests to their delightful 15th-century licensed restaurant, parts of which in fact date back to around 1320-1370, when it was the original Moot House (meeting place) of the village. Proprietors since 1979, their business has grown on the reputation for good food, service and value for money. There is also a fine selection of well-priced wines, several from the New World, to complement your meal. Attractive bar and lounge area. Patio garden. Ideal for small weddings and private parties.

LE TALBOOTH

Gun Hill, Dedham, nr Colchester. Tel: (01206) 323150, Fax: (01206) 322309

Hours: 12 to 2pm, 7 to 9pm daily.
Credit cards: Access, Visa, Amex.
Price guide: a la carte £30; table d'hote £18 & £21 (2 & 3 courses);
lunch £13.50 & £16 (2 & 3 courses). 10% service charge.
Accommodation: 10 luxurious suites at nearby Maison Talbooth (transport provided).

Examples from menus (revised two-monthly, table d'hote weekly): *finnan haddock & mushrooms topped with cheese souffle; panache of wild mushrooms scented with garlic set on carpaccio of potato; terrine of duck en croute with Cumberland sauce. Braised monkfish in potato coat on bed of leaf spinach; Indian vegetable curry; roast local partridge topped with liver paté. White chocolate tart "brulee"; ginger marmalade & advocaat syllabub; winter pudding.*

Now in its 44th year (all of them in the hands of the Milsom family), Le Talbooth is amongst England's most widely known and venerated restaurants. It is also one of the most depicted, being a stunning Tudor building beautifully situated on the banks of the River Stour in the heart of Constable Country. To sit out on the terrace under giant parasols is one of the joys of summer; log fires are winter's compensation, but the marvellous floodlit views can be enjoyed at any time. The menus afford a wide diversity to suit all palates, and prices are not unreasonable for a restaurant of this calibre. Spoil yourself further with a stay at the nearby Maison Talbooth - you won't forget it. You may also like to try the popular seafood restaurant The Pier at Harwich (qv), also owned by the family.

THE PIER RESTAURANT & HOTEL
The Quay, Harwich. Tel: (01255) 241212, Fax: (01255) 551922

Hours : 12 to 2pm, 6 to 9:30pm daily.
Credit cards : Access, Visa, Diners, Amex, Switch, Collect, Delta.
Price guide : a la carte £20, set price dinner £13.25 & £16.50 (2 & 3 courses); lunch £9.50 & £12.50 (2 & 3 courses); Sun. lunch £14.95. All subject to 10% service charge. Ha'penny Pier Bistro a la carte £11.50.
Accommodation : 6 dbls/twins (2 may be used as family). All en suite, TV, phone, tea & coffee, hair dryer on request. From £45 sngl, £62.50 dbl. Special 2- night break £155 per room (incl. £17.50pp dinner allowance).

Examples from menus (restaurant revised twice-monthly): *gateau of smoked chicken, avocado & soured cream; bisque of local lobster; terrine of spinach & vegetables. Baked fillet of local bass with fresh herb crust on lemon sauce; salmon & dill fish cakes; roasted rack of smoked lamb. Pina Colada cheesecake; almond & coconut tuile basket filled with white chocolate mousse on blackcurrant compote. Ha'penny Pier Bistro: fish & chips (speciality); fish pie; steaks; savoury veg. crumble.*

You could watch the seafood being landed on the quay on its very short journey to table, via chef/manager (for 17 years) Chris Oakley - one reason why this is one of the most celebrated restaurants in the area. Good, simple and inexpensive snacks may be had in the downstairs bistro. The view is always stunning, especially from the upstairs restaurant, but the nautical decor (a rich marine blue being the theme colour) is also diverting. None of the Victorian grandeur has been lost, and such a strangely quiet location (the town's narrow streets just to the rear) is a marvellous spot for an overnight stay or function (up to 80).

ALVARO'S

32 St. Helen's Road, Westcliff-on-Sea. Tel: (01702) 335840

Hours : 12 to 2pm Tues-Fri, 7 to 10:30pm Tues-Sun (11pm Fri & Sat).
Credit cards : Access, Visa.
Price guide : a la carte from £21.

Examples from menus (revised periodically): *langoustines sauteed in spicy Portuguese piri-piri butter; salted cod (with onion, potato, black olives & egg). Portuguese fish casserole; fillets of sole in light egg batter (pan-fried with banana, Madeira style), beef Alvaro's (large sirloin pan fried in butter with onions, mushrooms, artichokes, & wine, finished with brandy & cream); roast half duckling in port wine sauce; speciality espetadas. Crepes & flambes.*

The Portuguese are, like their oldest allies the English, a maritime nation, but their expertise in cooking with fish puts us to shame. There are no better exponents than Alvaro ('Freddy') Rodrigues and brother Jose (who cooks). Trained in Madeira, they have delighted palates here for over 19 years. Seafood is always to the fore, though steaks, pork, poultry etc, are well featured. The atmosphere and decor are also authentically Portuguese, with the theme of carved and painted cockerels, a legendary national symbol. Naturally, you will find a very fine range of Portuguese wines and old ports, but you may also like to try one of the unusual Portuguese beers. Service is attentive but unobtrusive. Rated highly by both national guides and local people, Alvaro's is just off the main shopping street; from the A127 or A13 take the first left by the lights at Victoria Station onto Hamlet Court Road, then third left - check when you book.

EDELWEISS SWISS RESTAURANT

1613 London Road, Leigh-on-Sea. Tel: (01702) 711517

Hours : 7 to 10pm, Mon. - Sat. Private lunches by arrangement.
Credit cards : Access, Visa, Amex.
Price guide : a la carte £26 - 28 (incl. drinks); 'Schnitzel' menu £12 (Mon - Thurs only).

Examples from menus (specials vary daily): *graubundner fleisch (air-cured beef served on wooden plate with black bread); coquilles d'homard "William Tell" (lobster meat served on shredded apple, lettuce with horseradish mayonnaise, boiled egg); Tournedo Heligoland (fillet steak filled with lobster, roasted with tarragon, in white wine cream sauce); Basler lummelbraten (fillet steak larded with pork fat, roasted & sliced with kidney, served with roast potatoes, celery & cream sauce); vegetarian dishes; flambes; fondues. Sweets & savouries.*

From land-locked mountainous Switzerland to the flat Essex coast - the contrast could hardly be starker, but chef patron Herbert Staudhammer has successfully recreated a little piece of his home country here over the past 16 years. He began in Zurich, garnering further experience from Germany, Paris and at the German Food Centre in Knightsbridge. These influences are brough to bear on his mouthwatering Franco-Germanic menus (only freshest ingredients), though he will be pleased to meet special 'exotic' requests if given sufficient notice - steak & kidney pudding and spotted dick are past examples! The cosy restaurant seats just 40, but there's only one sitting, so one may relax and perhaps share a fondue, a most sociable way of eating, accompanied perhaps by one of 14 uncommon Swiss wines.

211

THE DUKE OF YORK

Southend Road, Billericay (A 129) Tel: (01277) 651403

Hours : restaurant 12 to 2pm, 7 to 10pm Mon-Fri; 7 to 10pm Saturdays;
12 to 2:30pm Sundays. Pub OPEN ALL DAY.
Credit cards : Access, Visa, Diners, Amex.
Price guide : a la carte (also in French & German) £20 - £25. Table d'hote £16.
Bar meals from £3.85. Sunday lunch (roast £4.65). Booking advised.

Examples from menus: *courgettes provencal; smoked eel in garlic butter. Fillet of salmon in crab & mussel sauce; local trout Bretonne; strips of veal in tomato & cream sauce; supreme of chicken with bacon & cider sauce; strips of fillet steak in dill & coriander sauce; spinach & tomato roulade with hollandaise sauce; tandoori vegetables on bed of rice; grills; many daily specials. Crepes Suzettes; homemade sweets & gateaux. Trad. Sun. roasts. Bar: chicken Italienne; home-made pies; fresh skate; Cantonese prawns; fresh pasta dishes.*

Even though the menus are enormous, pride is taken in the freshness of all ingredients. Fish, for example, is delivered daily from the London markets, and some of the sweets and gateaux are made on the premises. Chef proprietor David White specialises in delicious sauces of all kinds, but will cook any dish to customer requirements - flexibility that is the stamp of a family-run business. Those who prefer their food without adornment have a wide choice of grilled meats and fish, and vegetarians have their own separate menu of at least 10 alternatives. Bar meals (except light snacks) may be take in the restaurant. Over 120 wines from all over the world are listed with helpful descriptions, and staff are all well trained in the subject - hence the Routiers '95 Corps d'Elite Award. An outstanding selection of malt whiskies would delight even the most discerning Scot! The antique cash register (in £. s. d.) will stir a little nostalgia.

LITTLE HAMMONDS
51 High Street, Ingatestone. Tel: (01277) 353194

Hours : 12 to 2:30pm, 6 to 11pm, 7 days per week (closed Bank Holiday
evenings).
Credit cards : Access, Visa, Switch.
Price guide : a la carte from £25.50 set price. Set lunch £17.50 Mon - Fri,
set dinner £17.50 Mon - Fri. Sunday lunch £12.95.

Examples from menus (revised quarterly, plus daily specials): *fruit terrine; pinwheel of salmon & tuna with Chartreuse dressing; chicken mousseline with basil, pan-fried & served with bacon sauce. Cod wrapped in parma ham, baked & served with saffron mashed potato; leg of lamb stuffed with stilton & apricot sat upon parsnip rosti; venison steak pan-fried & accompanied by game broth with julienne of beetroot; turned vegetables in spinach pancake with tomato sauce. Florentine sablée; flambé desserts.*

Proprietor Stuart Hammond acquired his expertise at various high class hotels and restaurants, and opened here in August 1987. The 'Little' refers to the cottage in which it is housed, which dates from 1558 (the history is described on the front of the menu), and is as charming as one could hope for. The old A12 has been bypassed, leaving the village to slumber peacefully, and sparing the ancient beams from the juggernauts. Head chef Kevin Hannaford offers several 'creations' (named after local villages) in a style that is a combination of the best new ideas in cooking, with French, classical and nouvelle cuisine ('nouvelle' being only in the garnish, not size of portions!). The restaurant has outstanding facilities for a special occasion: the 'Magic Cabaret' seats parties of 10, there is a no-smoking room seating 12 and another private room for 25. Stuart also runs a very professional outside catering service (tel. 352927) for all kinds of events. If the delicious aroma of fresh-baked bread wafts around you, that will be from his bakehouse next door!

RUSSELLS RESTAURANT

Bell Street, Gt Baddow, nr Chelmsford. Tel: (01245) 478484, Fax: (01245) 472705

Hours: 12 to 2pm, 7 to 11pm Tues - Sun. Mondays by prior arrangement.
Credit cards: Access, Visa, Diners, Amex, Switch.
Price guide: a la carte from £25 (5 courses), table d'hote £15.95 (5 courses, not Sat. evening), lunch £9.95 (3 courses).

Examples from menu (table d'hote revised weekly, a la carte four-monthly): *mousse of sole wrapped in leek with champagne sauce; terrine of vegetables with tomato & pepper coulis. Complimentary sorbet. Boned pussin stuffed with black pudding & haggis, with sweet brandy sauce; pan-fried king scallops with coral mousseline & basil butter sauce; filo pastry parcels filled with avocado & mushrooms on blue cheese sauce. Pear brulee tart; steamed ginger sponge with lemon & lime sauce; profiteroles filled with white chocolate ganache. Trad. Sun. roasts.*

For all the passing fads of recent years, the classical Anglo-French restaurant still occupies a prominent place. A skilled exponent, chef Mark Jeans prepares a menu of considerable diversity, among which are numbered many classic favourites, plus vegetarian alternatives, and the last Thursday of every month is Gourmet Night. The building itself is decidedly English; built in 1372 as a barn, it has a high vaulted ceiling, a plethora of beams and exposed bricks, and a gallery overlooking the main dining area. Proprietors Barry and Juliet Watson came here in June '91 and quickly made their mark. They are especially proud of their excellent 82-strong international wine list. Disabled and conference facilites. Outside catering a speciality.

THE FARMHOUSE FEAST

The Street, Roxwell, nr Chelmsford. Tel & Fax: (01245) 248583

Hours : 6:00 (6:30 Sats) to 9:30pm Tues-Sat. Lunches Tues-Fri, Sat & Sun by arrangement. OPEN CHRISTMAS DAY.

Credit cards : Visa.

Price guide : 5-course FARMHOUSE FEAST £24, 3-course lunches £12.50 (£9.50 for senior citizens), dinners £14.50. Discounts for early diners & senior citizens (not Sats). Special promotions for parties.

Examples from menus (revised weekly): *split pea & carrot soup; three-marinated herring. Breast of chicken filled with cream cheese & garlic, baked & served with port sauce; roast leg of lamb with apricot & almond sauce; wing of skate with black butter & capers; rice & pineapple croquettes with spicy peanut sauce. Blackberry & apple crumble with cream, ice cream or yoghurt; coffee & hazelnut roulade. Theme evenings eg: Starters & Puds monthly; Valentine; Mothering Sunday; Good Friday Vegetarian Gourmet.*

Half the menu is vegetarian, organic homegrown vegetables and wholefoods are used whenever possible, and everything is home-made, even the bread, cream cheese and petits fours. Chef patron Rosemary Upson is herself vegetarian, and is a regular in the major national guides. She offers an intriguing programme of special events - ask to go on the mailing list. But value for money is as important as healthy eating - there is a common misconception that quality restaurants like this are always expensive, but in fact you could well pay less than in a pub or pizza house. The farmhouse itself is 15th-century; exposed timbers divide off small, separate dining areas, cosy and warm - even the ghosts are reportedly friendly! Extensive wine list with weekly specials. No smoking area. Rooms available for private parties. Ideal for small weddings. Outside catering a speciality.

THE PUNCH BOWL

High Easter, nr Chelmsford. Tel: (01245) 231222/231264

Hours: 7pm to 9:30pm Tues - Sat, plus Sun. lunch.
Credit cards: Access, Visa, Amex.
Price guide: a la carte £22 (3 courses) midweek £18.90. Sun. lunch £15.90
(£7.50 for juniors - most welcome).

Examples from menus (revised seasonally): *Norfolk samphire; home-grown aspara-gus; moules mariniere. Filo pastry basket filled with smoked salmon, scrambled egg & cream; breast of duck with orange beurre blanc; individual beef Wellington; Cornish lobsters. Mrs Wright's butterscotch tart; champagne cocktails (speciality). Sunday lunch: roast sirloin of beef carved at the table.*

Consistency is surely a key to the long term success of any restaurant. Clearly the Punch Bowl possesses this quality in good measure, for it has remained amongst the county's best known and patronised for many years now. Youthful and energetic pro-prietors David and Penny Kelsey, together with their dedicated team, enjoy a large and loyal following, principally for good food on a diverse and interesting menu. Seven miles west of hectic Chelmsford, in a very different, more tranquil world, this Tudor building itself sets the stage: the 15th-century timbers and lovely solid willow floor are the backdrop for soft candlelight, fresh flowers and crisp linen. Many a memorable wedding reception has been held here, although in summer the marquee turns the two-acre garden into a set for 'Camelot' - very romantic. From this same garden come the fresh flowers and herbs for the kitchen; freshness is paramount in all ingredients. Over 200 wines. Outside catering a speciality.

GOODWILL GESTURE: PRESENT THIS GUIDE FOR COMPLIMENTARY PORT OR COGNAC

WOOLLCOTT HOUSE RESTAURANT

Anvil Cross, Gt Hallingbury, nr B. Stortford. Tel & Fax: (01279) 504397

Hours : 12 to 2pm (2:30 Suns), 7 to 10:30pm Wed - Sun; other times by arrangement.
Credit cards : Access, Visa, Switch.
Price guide : A la carte £22, table d'hote £15 (3 courses), lunch £12.95 (3 courses). Children half price.

Examples from menus (revised seasonally): *grilled goats' cheese with garlic croutons on seasonal salad; Scotch smoked salmon with capers & lemon. Fillets of sole filled with crab & scallops, with cream & white wine sauce; half roast Norfolk duckling with brandy & orange sauce; pan-fried calves' liver with lyonnaise onions & fresh creamed potato; daily specials. Thursday evenings: fresh fish & chips in trad. beer batter. Wednesday evening in Winter (excl Dec.) is Pudding Night. Trad. Sun. roasts (noted) £12.95.*

Taking drinks on the lawn is one of the civilised joys of summer, and here in pleasant countryside there is little to disturb the peace, despite the proximity of Stansted Airport. The house itself is only 12 years old, yet is beautifully proportioned and in keeping with the local style. A baby grand stands in one corner, there are flowers and crisp linen on each table, a handsome wooden fireplace and a large conservatory over-looking the seven acres of grounds. Food, too, is attractively presented; duck is a noted speciality (ring ahead to reserve), but special nights, such as Pasta, are also very pop-ular. There are regular dinner dances and occasionally a pianist or band performs - for details ask to go on the mailing list. Wedding receptions are a speciality; 95 can be seated inside (no room charge) or 200 in the marquee. Wines range from £9 up to £200, with some good value bin ends. Resident proprietors (since 1988) Jane and Robert (the chef) Woollcott pay close individual attention to their guests, in the way of the best family-run concerns.

217

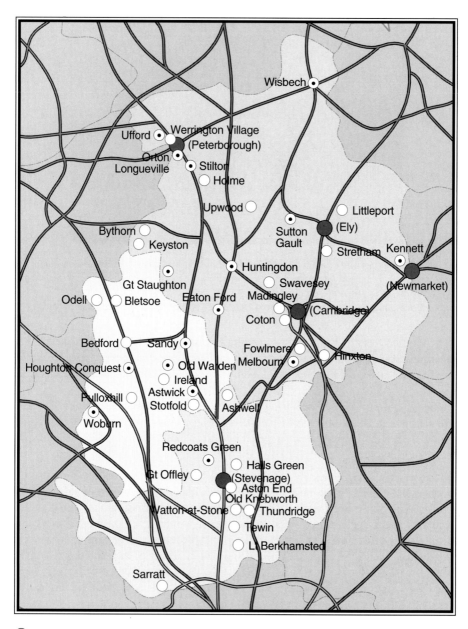

Wisbech

Ufford · Werrington Village
(Peterborough)
Orton
Longueville · Stilton
Holme
Upwood
Littleport
Bythorn
(Ely)
Keyston
Sutton
Gault Stretham Kennett
Huntingdon (Newmarket)
Swavesey
Gt Staughton Madingley
Odell Bletsoe Eaton Ford (Cambridge)
Coton
Bedford Sandy Fowlmere
Melbourn Hinxton
Houghton Conquest · Old Warden
Ireland
Pulloxhill Astwick ·
Stotfold Ashwell
Woburn
Redcoats Green
Halls Green
Gt Offley (Stevenage)
Aston End
Old Knebworth
Watton-at-Stone Thundridge
Tewin
Lt Berkhamsted
Sarratt

● Accommodation

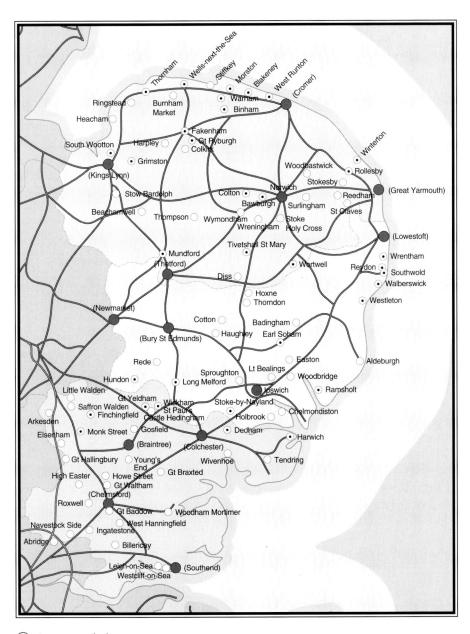

● Accommodation

Bedfordshire

Cambridgeshire

* Accommodation

Essex

Hertfordshire

Norfolk

* Accommodation

Suffolk